The Ultimate Visual Guide

Flowering Plants

WINDMILL
BOOKS

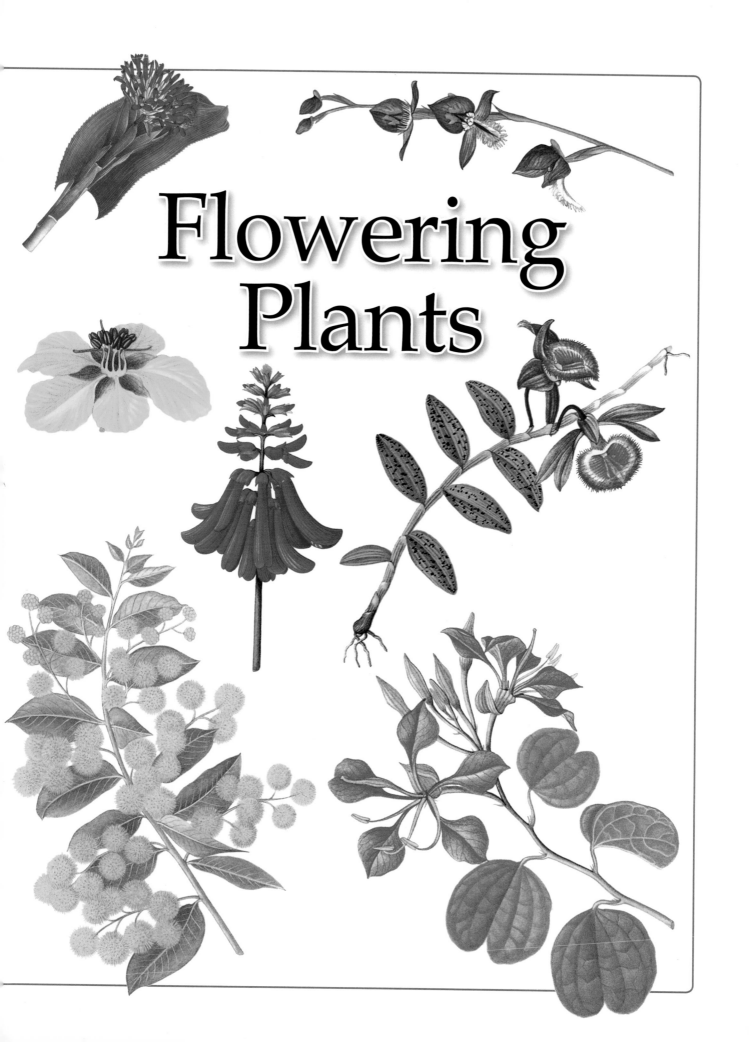

Flowering Plants

Windmill Books Ltd
First Floor
9-17 St. Albans Place
London N1 0NX
www.windmillbooks.co.uk

ISBN: 978-1-78121-132-8

Designer: Malcolm Parchment
Design Manager: Keith Davis
Production: Richard Berry
Production Consultant: Alastair Gourlay
Editors: Rod Green, Camilla Hallinan, Dawn Titmus
Managing Editor: Tim Harris
Editorial Director: Lindsey Lowe

Printed in China

INTRODUCTION

There are few things in the natural world that can match the beauty of a rose or an orchid in bloom. This book is a celebration of the world's flowering plants, from sunflowers to sundews, magnolias to mallows, and lilies to lilacs. While some of these groups are familiar as ornamentals, hundreds of less well-known plants also boast impressive blooms—and other more modest flowers are nevertheless things of beauty. This book has more than 1,000 glorious and accurate illustrations, most in full color, depicting hundreds of representatives of 145 plant families. Included are not only the bright and bold, but also those of great economic importance—the grass, potato, tobacco, and grapevine families, for example.

An introduction explains the anatomical terms used in the text, and the different forms that flowers, inflorescences, fruits, seeds, leaves, and root structures can take. There is a diagrammatic explanation of fertilization in a typical flowering plant.

The pages that follow showcase a wonderful selection of flowering plants from every corner of the world. Each family (or families) has a brief introduction, describing its nature, where the plants grow, and any special features they possess. The art depicts whole plants and details of flowers, fruits, and leaves. Each illustrated species has a caption (with the plant's scientific name), while annotations highlight details of particular interest.

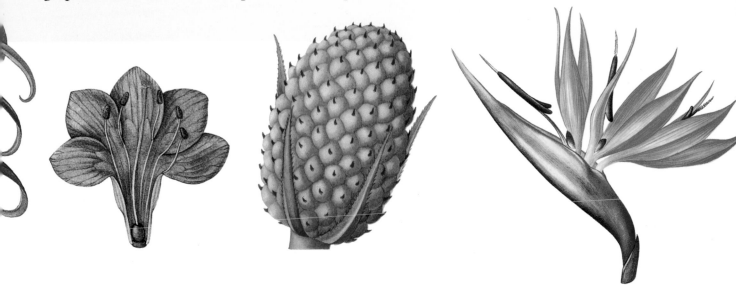

CONTENTS

THE MONOCOTYLEDONS

THE ANATOMY OF FLOWERS

Many of the different species of plants featured in this book share a common anatomy but there are often notable differences. The illustrations on these pages help to identify the different parts of the plants and explain some of the terminology used.

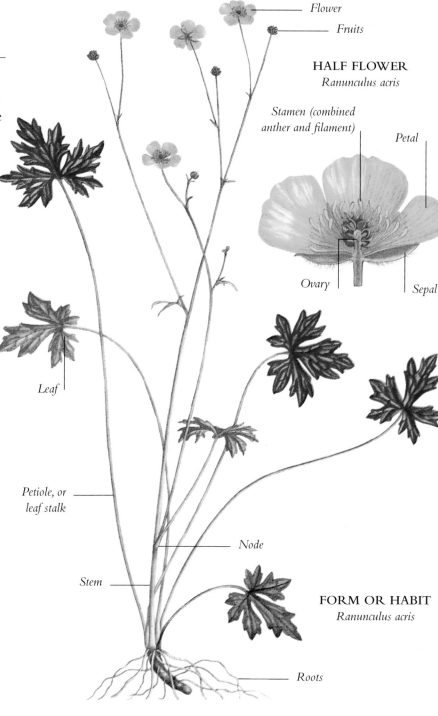

Flower

Fruits

HALF FLOWER
Ranunculus acris

Stamen (combined anther and filament)

Petal

Ovary

Sepal

Leaf

Petiole, or leaf stalk

Node

Stem

FORM OR HABIT
Ranunculus acris

Roots

COMMON FORMS OF MONOCOTYLEDON FLOWERS

Petals free

Corolla regular
Tradescantia

Corolla irregular
Zingiber

Petals (or perianth) fused

Regular
Lilium

Irregular
Oncidium

Petals (or perianth) absent

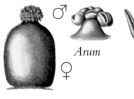

Arum

Hordeum

ARRANGEMENT OF FLORAL PARTS

Hypogynous
Ranunculus

Perigynous
Prunus

Epigynous
Chaenomeles

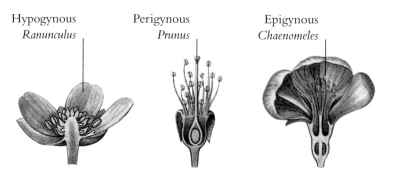

COMMON FORMS OF DICOTYLEDON FLOWERS

Petals free

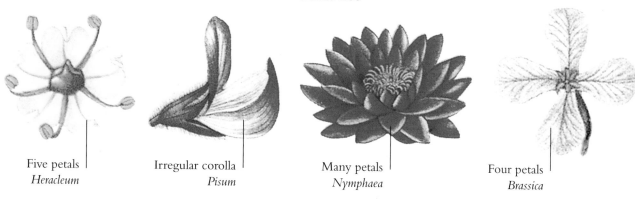

Five petals
Heracleum

Irregular corolla
Pisum

Many petals
Nymphaea

Four petals
Brassica

Petals fused

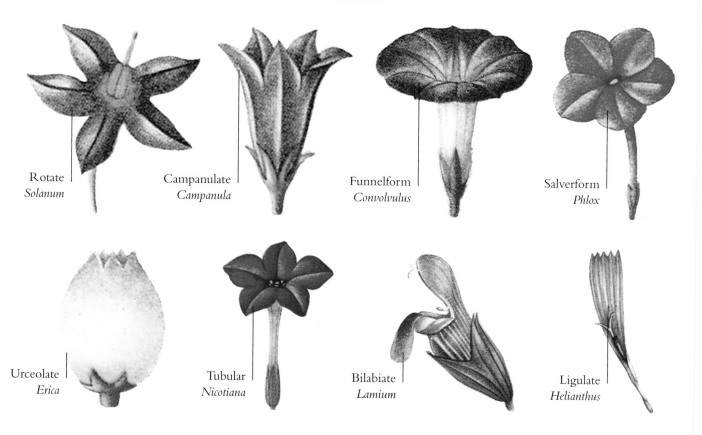

Rotate
Solanum

Campanulate
Campanula

Funnelform
Convolvulus

Salverform
Phlox

Urceolate
Erica

Tubular
Nicotiana

Bilabiate
Lamium

Ligulate
Helianthus

Petals (or perianth) absent

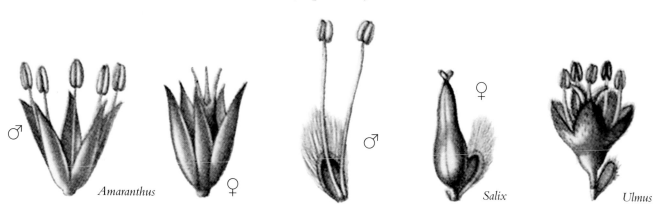

Amaranthus

Salix

Ulmus

FRUITS AND SEEDS

Flowering plants produce fruits, which usually develop from the ovaries but sometimes from other tissues. Some fruits, such as berries, have evolved to be particularly appealing to animals, which eat the fruit and then distribute the seeds in their droppings. Other fruits, such as rambutans, have spines that attach to an animal's coat to aid seed distribution, while some, such as sycamores, release their seeds to be carried on the wind.

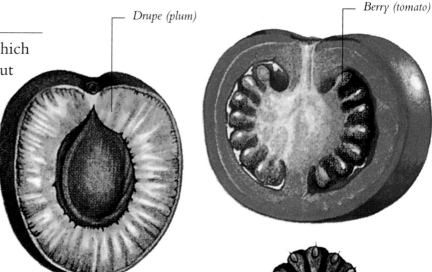

Drupe (plum)

Berry (tomato)

Aggregation of drupes (blackberry)

Pome (apple)

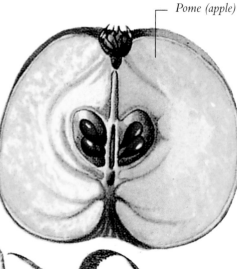

FLESHY MULTIPLE FRUITS
These fruits are derived from an inflorescence, an arrangement of more than one flower such as a raceme or a panicle.

Pseudocarp (strawberry)

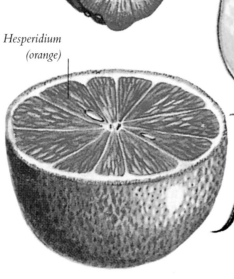

Hesperidium (orange)

Syconium (fig)

Coenocarpium (pineapple)

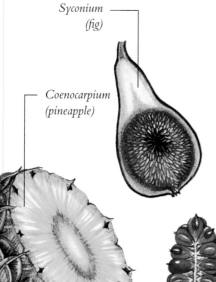

Sorosis (mulberry)

Hep (rose)

FLESHY FRUITS
These fruits are derived from a single flower, although many flowers may appear on the host plant.

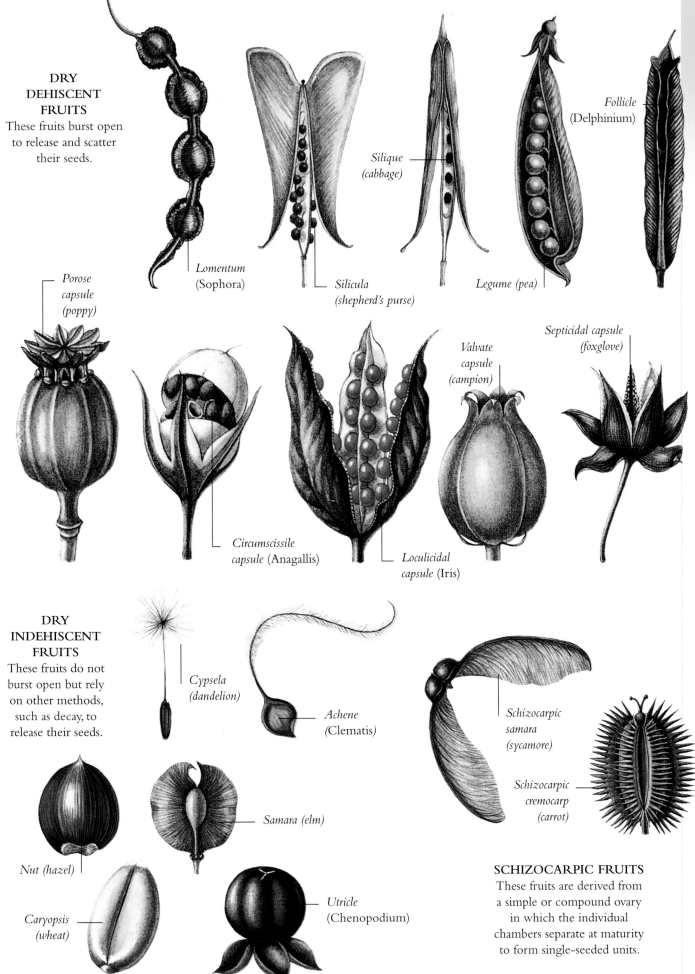

DRY DEHISCENT FRUITS
These fruits burst open to release and scatter their seeds.

Lomentum (Sophora)

Silique (cabbage)

Silicula (shepherd's purse)

Legume (pea)

Follicle (Delphinium)

Porose capsule (poppy)

Circumscissile capsule (Anagallis)

Loculicidal capsule (Iris)

Valvate capsule (campion)

Septicidal capsule (foxglove)

DRY INDEHISCENT FRUITS
These fruits do not burst open but rely on other methods, such as decay, to release their seeds.

Cypsela (dandelion)

Achene (Clematis)

Schizocarpic samara (sycamore)

Schizocarpic cremocarp (carrot)

Samara (elm)

Nut (hazel)

Caryopsis (wheat)

Utricle (Chenopodium)

SCHIZOCARPIC FRUITS
These fruits are derived from a simple or compound ovary in which the individual chambers separate at maturity to form single-seeded units.

FRUITS OF GOURDS AND LEGUMES

The plants featured here from the gourd and legume families include many food crops that are familiar from supermarket shelves and market stalls all over the world. Before their fruits mature—indeed, before they even appear—the plants display a variety of different flowers, which are necessary for fertilization and which later develop into the fruits.

MARROWS, GOURDS, AND OTHER RELATIVES
Family Cucurbitaceae
This highly specialized family of mainly climbing plants and ground creepers provides food sources as apparently different as the Honeydew Melon and the Gherkin.

1. Netted melon, *Cucumis melo;* 2. Cucumber, *Cucumis sativus;* 3. Zucchini, *Cucurbita pepo;* 4. Summer Squash, *Cucurbita pepo;* 5. Pumpkin, *Cucurbita moschata;* 6. Winter Squash, *Cucurbita mixta;* 7. Honeydew Melon, *Cucumis melo;* 8. Pattypan Squash, *Cucurbita pepo;* 9. Watermelon, *Citrulllus lanatus;* 10. Vegetable Marrow, *Cucurbita pepo.*

1. Scarlet Runner Bean, *Phaseolus coccineus*; 2. Kidney Bean, *Phaseolus vulgaris*; 3. Haricot Bean, *Phaseolus vulgaris*; 4. French Bean, *Phaseolus vulgaris*; 5. Lentil, *Lens culinaris*; 6. Broad Bean, *Vicia faba*; 7. Garden Pea, *Pisum sativum*; 8. Asparagus Pea, *Tetragonolobus purpureus*.

BEANS, LENTILS, AND PEAS
Family Leguminosae
The legumes are an enormously important group, with the seeds and pods of many of the herbaceous species providing mineral- and protein-rich food for humans and animals. Other species can be plowed into the soil, functioning as an excellent fertilizer by boosting nitrogen levels.

LEAVES AND PLANT STRUCTURE

Plants use most leaves for photosynthesis, turning energy from sunlight into chemical energy that the plant needs to grow and to reproduce. Leaves are also the plant's "lungs," absorbing carbon dioxide from the atmosphere and expelling oxygen, a byproduct of the chemical reactions taking place within the plant. A plant's flowers generally contain its sex organs and are vital for producing the fruit and seeds it uses to reproduce. The structure and appearance of those organs can vary enormously.

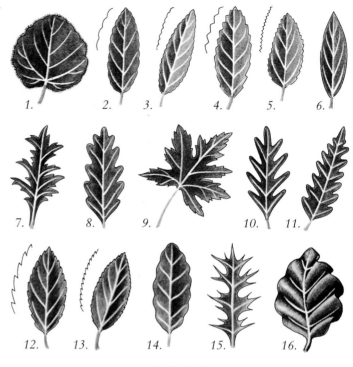

MARGINS
1. Ciliate; 2. Crenate; 3. Crenulate; 4. Dentate; 5. Denticulate; 6. Entire; 7. Incised; 8. Lobed; 9. Palmately lobed; 10. Pinnately lobed; 11. Pinnatisect; 12. Serrate; 13. Serrulate; 14. Sinuate; 15. Spinose; 16. Undulate

COMPOUND LEAVES
1. Bipinnate; 2. Imparipinnate; 3. Palmate; 4. Paripinnate; 5. Trifoliolate; 6. Unifoliolate

VEIN STRUCTURE
1. Palmate; 2. Parallel; 3. Pinnate

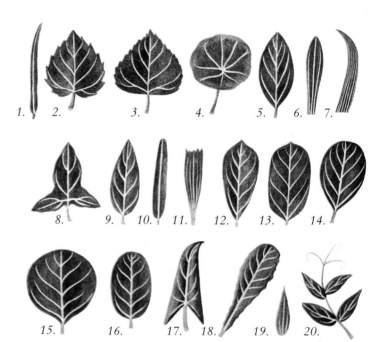

SHAPES
1. Acicular; 2. Cordate; 3. Deltoid; 4. Peltate; 5. Elliptic; 6. Ensiform; 7. Falcate; 8. Hastate; 9. Lanceolate; 10. Linear; 11. Ligulate; 12. Oblanceolate; 13. Oblong; 14. Obovate; 15. Orbicular; 16. Oval; 17. Sagittate; 18. Spatulate; 19. Subulate; 20. Tendril

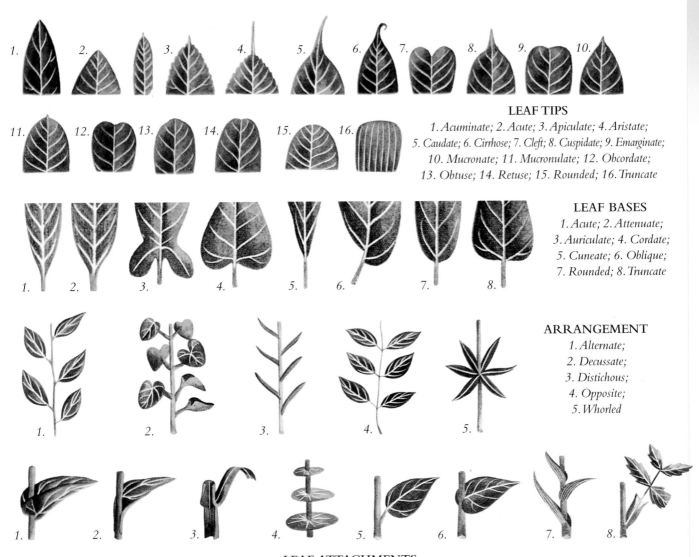

LEAF TIPS
1. Acuminate; 2. Acute; 3. Apiculate; 4. Aristate;
5. Caudate; 6. Cirrhose; 7. Cleft; 8. Cuspidate; 9. Emarginate;
10. Mucronate; 11. Mucronulate; 12. Obcordate;
13. Obtuse; 14. Retuse; 15. Rounded; 16. Truncate

LEAF BASES
1. Acute; 2. Attenuate;
3. Auriculate; 4. Cordate;
5. Cuneate; 6. Oblique;
7. Rounded; 8. Truncate

ARRANGEMENT
1. Alternate;
2. Decussate;
3. Distichous;
4. Opposite;
5. Whorled

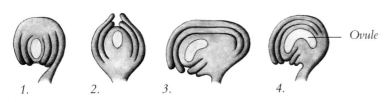

LEAF ATTACHMENTS
1. Amplexicaul; 2. Decurrent; 3. Ligulate; 4. Perfoliate;
5. Petiolate; 6. Sessile 7. Sheathing 8. Stipulate

Ovule

Stamen

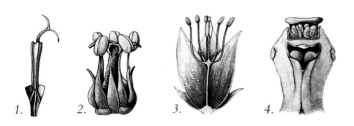

MAIN TYPES OF OVULES
1. Anatropous; 2. Orthotropous; 3. Campylotropous; 4. Amphitropous

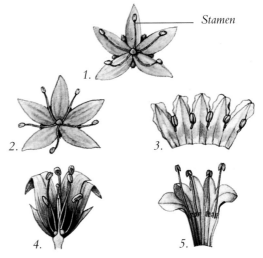

ANDROECIUM TYPES
1. Syngenesious; 2. With staminodes; 3. Gynandrophore; 4. Column

STAMEN ARRANGEMENT
1. Antipetalous; 2. Antisepalous; 3. Epipetalous;
4. Didynamous; 5. Tetradynamous

TYPES OF INFLORESCENCE

An inflorescence is any arrangement of more than one flower. The main types of inflorescence are divided into three categories: cymose, racemose, and mixed. In a cymose inflorescence, each terminal growing point produces a flower, while a racemose inflorescence is capable of indefinite prolongation and bears both axillary (arising at the junction of the stem and leaf) and lateral flowers. Mixed infloresence, such as a catkin or thyrse, bears both.

1.

CYMOSE INFLORESCENCES
Monochasia
A monochasium is a cymose inflorescence in which there is a single terminal flower with a single branch below it bearing flowers.

Monochasia:
1. Simple
2. Bostryx
3. Drepanium
4. Cincinnus
5. Rhipidium

2.

3.

4.

5.

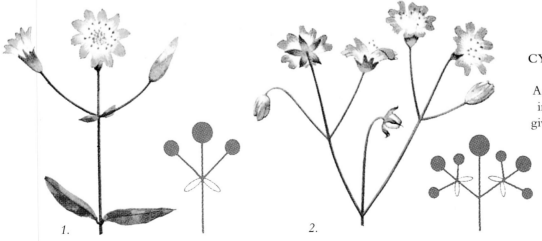

1.

2.

CYMOSE INFLORESCENCES
Dichasia
A dichasium is a form of cymose inflorescence with each branch giving rise to two other branches.

Dichasia:
1. Simple
2. Compound

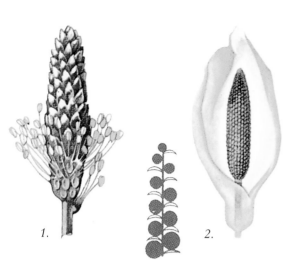

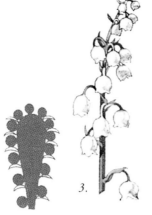

RACEMOSE INFLORESCENCES

These consist of a main axis bearing single flowers alternately, or spirally, on stalks of roughly equal length. Since the apical growing point is active, there is usually no terminal flower.

Racemose inflorescences:
1. Spike
2. Spadix
3. Raceme
4. Corymb
5. Panicle
6. Simple umbel
7. Compound umbel
8. Capitulum (head)

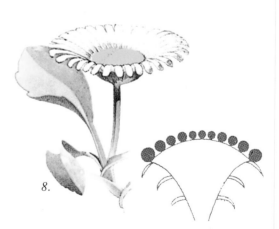

MIXED INFLORESCENCES

This type of inflorescence displays both cymose and racemose branching.

Mixed inflorescences:
1. Catkins
2. Thyrse
3. Verticillaster

FERTILIZATION

Fertilization takes place when male and female reproductive cells, or gametes, fuse in the ovary after pollination. Cross-fertilization occurs between flowers from separate plants; self-fertilization takes place between flowers on the same plant or within the same flower.

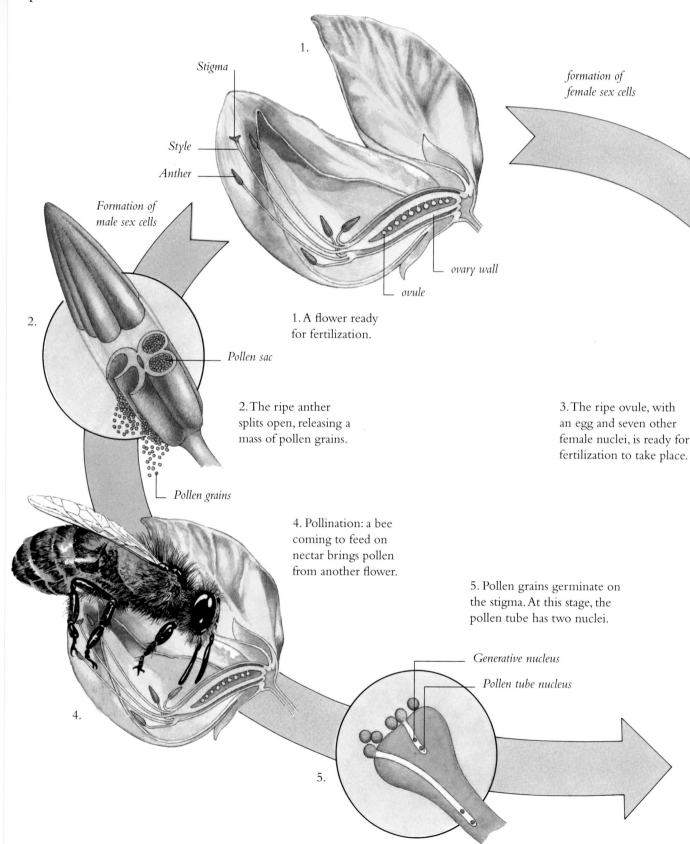

Stigma

Style

Anther

Formation of male sex cells

Pollen sac

Pollen grains

1.

formation of female sex cells

ovary wall

ovule

2.

4.

5.

Generative nucleus

Pollen tube nucleus

1. A flower ready for fertilization.

2. The ripe anther splits open, releasing a mass of pollen grains.

3. The ripe ovule, with an egg and seven other female nuclei, is ready for fertilization to take place.

4. Pollination: a bee coming to feed on nectar brings pollen from another flower.

5. Pollen grains germinate on the stigma. At this stage, the pollen tube has two nuclei.

STAGES OF FERTILIZATION

Fertilization is the meeting of male and female sex cells. In a plant, these are the male nuclei from a pollen grain and the plant's eggs (ova). When pollen arrives on the stigma, it germinates, growing a tiny tube down the style toward the ovary. At first, the pollen grain contains two nuclei, the pollen tube nucleus (which controls the growth of the pollen tube) and the generative nucleus.

As the tube reaches the ovary, the generative nucleus divides to produce two male nuclei (the equivalent of sperm in an animal). The pollen tube enters an ovule and releases the two male nuclei. One of them fuses with the egg. This is the process of fertilization. The fertilized egg then divides many times to make the embryo. The second male nucleus fuses with two other cells in the ovule to form a cell that gives rise to a tissue called the endosperm, which supplies nutrients to the developing embryo.

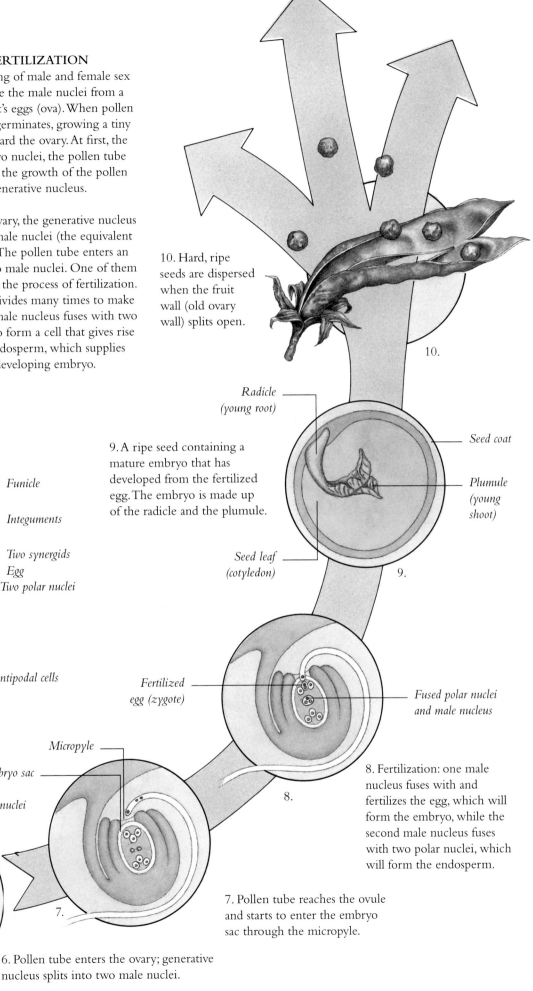

10. Hard, ripe seeds are dispersed when the fruit wall (old ovary wall) splits open.

10.

Radicle (young root)

Seed coat

9. A ripe seed containing a mature embryo that has developed from the fertilized egg. The embryo is made up of the radicle and the plumule.

Plumule (young shoot)

Seed leaf (cotyledon)

9.

Funicle

Integuments

Two synergids

Egg

Two polar nuclei

3.

Three antipodal cells

Fertilized egg (zygote)

Fused polar nuclei and male nucleus

8. Fertilization: one male nucleus fuses with and fertilizes the egg, which will form the embryo, while the second male nucleus fuses with two polar nuclei, which will form the endosperm.

Micropyle

Embryo sac

Two male nuclei

8.

7. Pollen tube reaches the ovule and starts to enter the embryo sac through the micropyle.

7.

6. Pollen tube enters the ovary; generative nucleus splits into two male nuclei.

6.

ACANTHUS AND AMARANTHS

The acanthus family (Acanthaceae) is made up of herbs, shrubs, and climbers, as well as some large trees, including several mangroves. Most acanthus grow in the tropics and subtropics. Amaranths (Amaranthaceae) are mostly tropical herbs and shrubs, containing the grain amaranths of Central and South America, and several species of horticultural importance.

REDROOT AMARANTH
Amaranthus retroflexus
This plant grows to 3–6 feet (0.9–1.8 m) tall and has a leafy shoot with small green flowers in axillary tassels.

SLENDER SNAKECOTTON
Froelichia gracilis
This plant has shoots with large, lateral, hairy, sterile flowers.

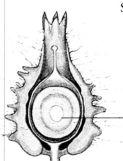

Vertical section through a sterile flower

SHRUBBY DEERINGIA
Deeringia amaranthoides
This treetop vine or climbing shrub produces stems that can be up to 20 feet (6.1 m) long.

Red fruits lie at the base of the stem

SHORELINE SEA PURSLANE
Sesuvium portulacastrum
This shrub in the amaranth family has a jointed, succulent stem with opposite leaves and campanulate flowers.

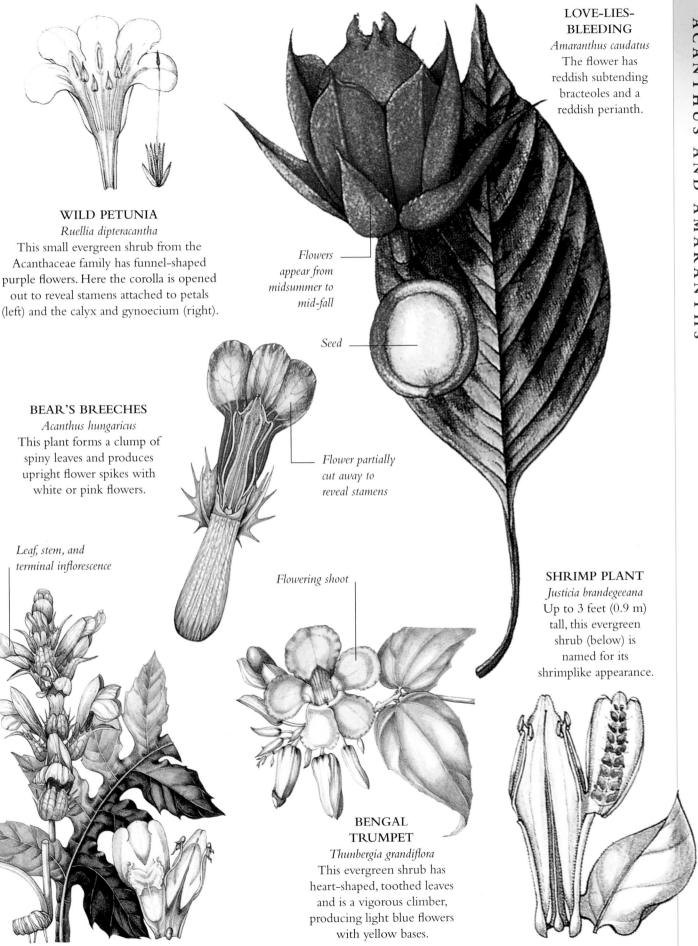

WILD PETUNIA
Ruellia dipteracantha
This small evergreen shrub from the Acanthaceae family has funnel-shaped purple flowers. Here the corolla is opened out to reveal stamens attached to petals (left) and the calyx and gynoecium (right).

LOVE-LIES-BLEEDING
Amaranthus caudatus
The flower has reddish subtending bracteoles and a reddish perianth.

Flowers appear from midsummer to mid-fall

Seed

BEAR'S BREECHES
Acanthus hungaricus
This plant forms a clump of spiny leaves and produces upright flower spikes with white or pink flowers.

Flower partially cut away to reveal stamens

Leaf, stem, and terminal inflorescence

Flowering shoot

SHRIMP PLANT
Justicia brandegeeana
Up to 3 feet (0.9 m) tall, this evergreen shrub (below) is named for its shrimplike appearance.

BENGAL TRUMPET
Thunbergia grandiflora
This evergreen shrub has heart-shaped, toothed leaves and is a vigorous climber, producing light blue flowers with yellow bases.

CASHEWS AND MANGOS

Of great economic importance for their fruits, cashews and mangos (Anacardiaceae) are largely tropical and subtropical trees and shrubs. The family has a more or less equal representation in South America, Africa, and Asia. A few genera are native to temperate North America and Eurasia.

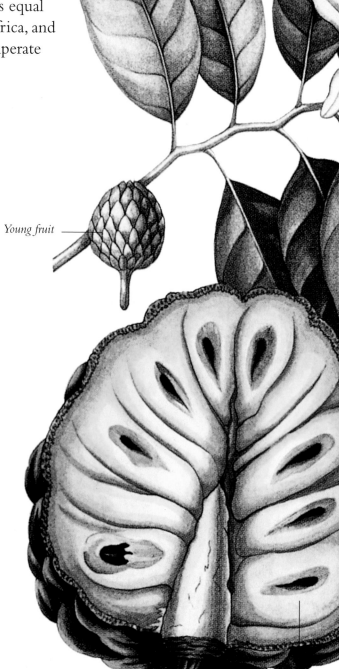

Young fruit

MASTIC TREE
Pistacia lentiscus
This evergreen shrub can grow up to 16 feet (4.9 m) tall. It produces a sweet resin, which is sometimes used to flavor deserts and candy.

Male flower with short, lobed calyx and stamens with short filaments

Vertical section through a Mastic Tree fruit

Vertical section through Sugar Apple fruit showing an aggregate of numerous berries with the fleshy receptacle

*Sugar Apple shoot with
leaves in two ranks
and axillary flower*

*Flower with petals, stamens,
and one sepal removed to
show thickened style*

*Corolla opened
out, showing
stamens*

SUGAR APPLE
Annona squamosa
This small deciduous tree
grows up to 26 feet (7.9 m)
and produces edible fruits
that give the plant its
common name.

*Ancistrocladus
heyneanus fruit
(a nut) surrounded
by persistent calyx*

ANCISTROCLADUS VAHLII
Found in tropical forests and swamps, this
climbing, twining liana has flowering shoots
with hooked tips, rosettes of simple alternate
leaves, and flowers in a loose inflorescence.

Cashew fruit

*Section
through fruit*

CALABASH NUTMEG
Monodora myristica
This large tropical tree
produces scented,
red-spotted flowers
and huge leaves.

CASHEW TREE
Anacardium occidentale
The nut is a seed inside the
kidney-shaped fruit below
a pear-shaped receptacle.
The leaves are simple in shape.

CARROTS

Most members of the carrot family
(Apiaceae) are herbaceous plants with
hollow internodes. They have characteristic
umbelliferous (umbrella-like) inflorescences
and some have edible fruits. Several species
develop some degree of woodiness, and
geniunely woody, treelike, or shrubby
species also exist.

Regular flowers
at center of
inflorescences

Leaves can reach
20 inches (50 cm)
in length

COMMON HOGWEED
Heracleum sphondylium
This plant produces large
inflorescences, the outer
flowers of which are
irregular and have
deeply cut petals.

Regular
hogweed
flower

CARROT
Daucus carota
The only member of the family
that is a major vegetable crop, this
plant produces a schizocarp with
spines on the ridges.

Long-stalked,
rounded leaves

Flowers grow
close to the
surface of
the soil

SPADELEAF
Centella asiatica
This small herbaceous plant grows
in low, wet areas throughout India
and Southeast Asia.

Roots growing
from creeping
stems

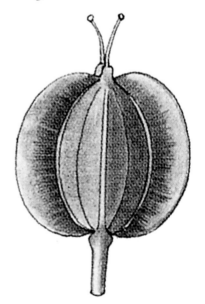

MASTERWORT
Peucedanum ostruthium
This plant is found in woodlands,
damp fields, river banks, and
mountain meadows. It produces
thin, winged schizocarps.

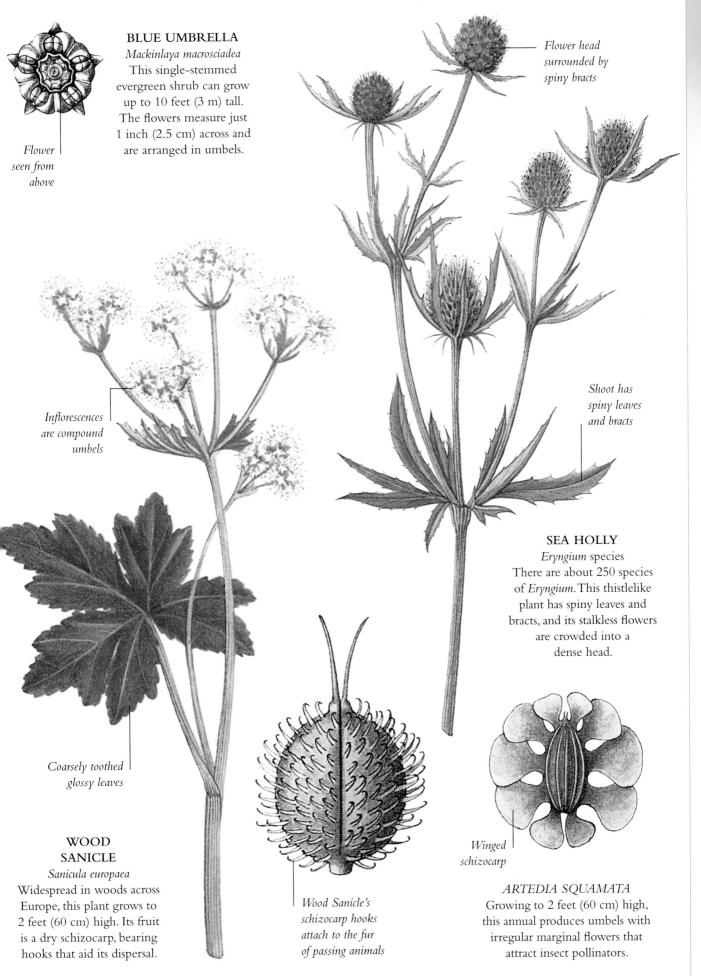

BLUE UMBRELLA
Mackinlaya macrosciadea
This single-stemmed
evergreen shrub can grow
up to 10 feet (3 m) tall.
The flowers measure just
1 inch (2.5 cm) across and
are arranged in umbels.

*Flower
seen from
above*

*Flower head
surrounded by
spiny bracts*

*Inflorescences
are compound
umbels*

*Shoot has
spiny leaves
and bracts*

SEA HOLLY
Eryngium species
There are about 250 species
of *Eryngium*. This thistlelike
plant has spiny leaves and
bracts, and its stalkless flowers
are crowded into a
dense head.

*Coarsely toothed
glossy leaves*

*Winged
schizocarp*

**WOOD
SANICLE**
Sanicula europaea
Widespread in woods across
Europe, this plant grows to
2 feet (60 cm) high. Its fruit
is a dry schizocarp, bearing
hooks that aid its dispersal.

*Wood Sanicle's
schizocarp hooks
attach to the fur
of passing animals*

ARTEDIA SQUAMATA
Growing to 2 feet (60 cm) high,
this annual produces umbels with
irregular marginal flowers that
attract insect pollinators.

OLEANDERS AND MILKWEEDS

The Apocynaceae family comprises a variety of trees, shrubs, woody lianas, vines, and herbs. Most are perennial, though others are annual or even ephemeral. Growing wild throughout the tropics and subtropics, some of these plants are highly toxic and traditionally have been used to create poison for arrow tips. Other species are used to make medicines—Madagascar Periwinkle (*Catharanthus roseus*) for cancer-treatment drugs, for example.

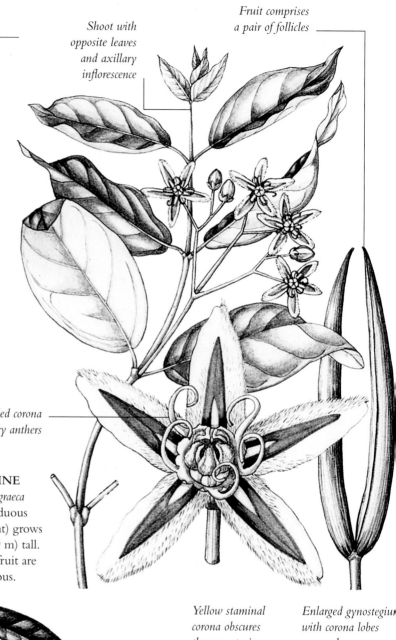

Shoot with opposite leaves and axillary inflorescence

Fruit comprises a pair of follicles

Flower has coiled corona lobes and hairy anthers

SILK VINE
Periploca graeca
This deciduous climber (right) grows to 30 feet (9 m) tall. Its sap and fruit are poisonous.

Yellow staminal corona obscures the gynostegium

Enlarged gynostegium with corona lobes removed

BLOODFLOWER
Asclepias curassavica
Also known as Tropical Milkweed or Butterfly Weed, this evergreen shrub produces clusters of red-and-yellow flowers (shown right) that are attractive to butterflies.

Seed with tuft of hairs to help dispersal by the wind

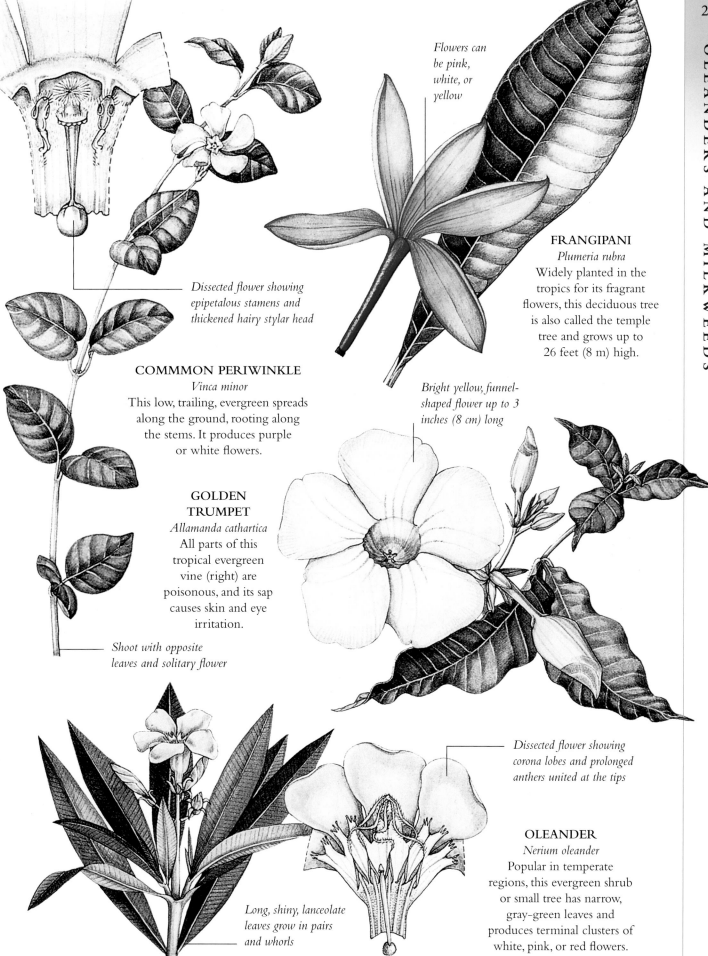

Flowers can be pink, white, or yellow

Dissected flower showing epipetalous stamens and thickened hairy stylar head

FRANGIPANI
Plumeria rubra
Widely planted in the tropics for its fragrant flowers, this deciduous tree is also called the temple tree and grows up to 26 feet (8 m) high.

COMMMON PERIWINKLE
Vinca minor
This low, trailing, evergreen spreads along the ground, rooting along the stems. It produces purple or white flowers.

Bright yellow, funnel-shaped flower up to 3 inches (8 cm) long

GOLDEN TRUMPET
Allamanda cathartica
All parts of this tropical evergreen vine (right) are poisonous, and its sap causes skin and eye irritation.

Shoot with opposite leaves and solitary flower

Dissected flower showing corona lobes and prolonged anthers united at the tips

OLEANDER
Nerium oleander
Popular in temperate regions, this evergreen shrub or small tree has narrow, gray-green leaves and produces terminal clusters of white, pink, or red flowers.

Long, shiny, lanceolate leaves grow in pairs and whorls

HOLLIES, IVIES, AND GINSENG

Hollies (Aquifoliaceae) are widespread but mainly tropical trees and shrubby plants. Many are grown for their foliage and used as ornamental plants. Their leaves are often leathery with dentate, prickly edges; they are usually evergreen, only rarely deciduous. The ivies and ginseng (Araliaceae) are also largely tropical and, like hollies, they produce small flowers and drupes (fruits with stones).

Leaves alternate on the stem, seldom growing directly opposite

Gynoecium with sessile stigma

Female flower with four sterile stamens

Corolla of male flower opened out

Drupaceous fruit

ENGLISH HOLLY
Ilex aquifolium
Also known as Common Holly or Christmas Holly, more than 400 species of *Ilex* are found around the world.

OCTOPUS CABBAGE TREE
Cussonia arborea
Native to tropical Africa, this deciduous plant can grow to 36 feet (11 m) high or more.

Part of influrescence

Fruit

Part of stem crowned by fruiting head

Flowers in umbels

Cross section of fruit

Cordate adult leaves are unlobed

ENGLISH IVY
Hedera helix
This rampant evergreen vine with alternate leaves clings to trees or walls and can climb to around 100 feet (30.5 m) high.

Ivy's palmate young leaves have five lobes

Stipulate trifoliate leaves

HENRY'S FINGER
Eleutherococcus henryi
This deciduous shrub has trailing branches and terminal clusters of black fruits.

Henry's finger vertical section of ovary

Pinnate leaves of Aralia scopulorum

Ivy's climbing shoots have aerial rootlets for grip

SUNFLOWERS

Sunflowers (Asteraceae) are some of the best-known flowering plant families, growing on all continents apart from Antarctica. They grow in semiarid regions of the tropics and subtropics as well as in alpine, temperate, and Arctic zones, although they do not thrive in tropical rain forests. They may be annual or perennial herbs, shrubs, climbers, or small trees. Marigolds, dahlias, and chrysanthemums are grown as ornamentals.

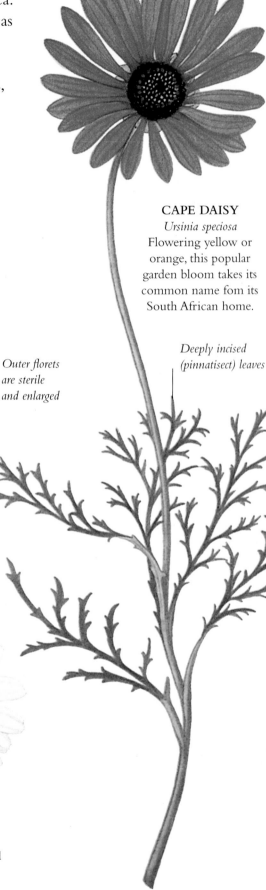

CAPE DAISY
Ursinia speciosa
Flowering yellow or orange, this popular garden bloom takes its common name fom its South African home.

Deeply incised (pinnatisect) leaves

SWAMP SUNFLOWER
Helianthus angustifolius
Native to the United States, this plant thrives in damp areas along Atlantic and Gulf of Mexico coasts.

Outer florets are sterile and enlarged

LEMON-SCENTED EDELWEISS
Leontopodium haplophylloides
Up to 12 inches (30 cm) tall, this alpine plant blooms with white bracts in late spring or early summer.

MARGUERITE
Argyranthemum broussonetii
Available in several varieties and cultivars, Marguerites produce prolific, daisylike flowers.

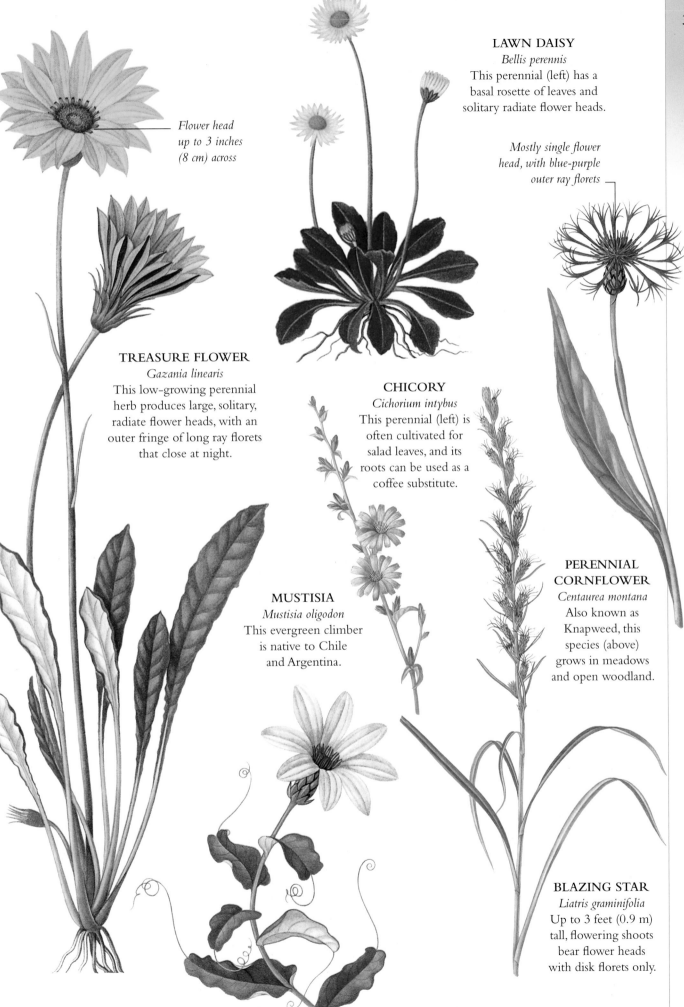

*Flower head
up to 3 inches
(8 cm) across*

LAWN DAISY
Bellis perennis
This perennial (left) has a
basal rosette of leaves and
solitary radiate flower heads.

*Mostly single flower
head, with blue-purple
outer ray florets*

TREASURE FLOWER
Gazania linearis
This low-growing perennial
herb produces large, solitary,
radiate flower heads, with an
outer fringe of long ray florets
that close at night.

CHICORY
Cichorium intybus
This perennial (left) is
often cultivated for
salad leaves, and its
roots can be used as a
coffee substitute.

**PERENNIAL
CORNFLOWER**
Centaurea montana
Also known as
Knapweed, this
species (above)
grows in meadows
and open woodland.

MUSTISIA
Mustisia oligodon
This evergreen climber
is native to Chile
and Argentina.

BLAZING STAR
Liatris graminifolia
Up to 3 feet (0.9 m)
tall, flowering shoots
bear flower heads
with disk florets only.

BEGONIAS AND SPOTTED LAURELS

The begonias (Begoniaceae) are semi-succulent herbs, with asymmetrical, fleshy leaves. Native to the tropics, begonias are also cultivated in temperate regions as ornamentals. Spotted laurels (Aucubaceae) are usually evergreen, ornamental shrubs or small trees, with leaves up to 10 inches (25 cm). Largely tropical, the Balanophoraceae is a family of root parasites that do not contain chlorophyll (they are achlorophyllous).

Male flower buds

Female flowers showing five perianth segments

Male flower

Habit showing leaves with stipules and axillary inflorescences

Young winged fruit

Winged fruit cross section

REX BEGONIA
Begonia rex
Growing to 12 inches (30 cm), this evergreen, rhizomatous perennial is prized for its foliage rather than its small flowers.

Leaf is green with silvery zone on surface, reddish beneath

Leafy shoot and female flowers

Male flower

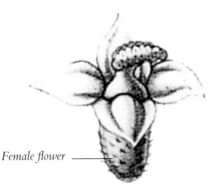

Female flower

JAPANESE LAUREL
Aucuba japonica
This evergreen shrub has glossy, broadly elliptical, serrated leaves that are alternate, simple, and green or mottled yellow. The fruit is a colorful, ovoid berry.

Cross section of fruit shows a single seed

LOPHOPHYTUM WEDDELLII
The *Lophophytum* genus of root parasites (they attach to the roots of their hosts) is found in the lowland rain forests of tropical South America.

Aerial male inflorescence, which stems from an underground tuber

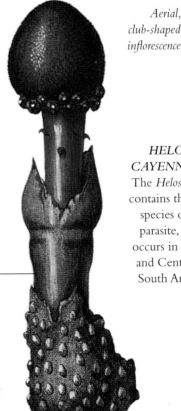

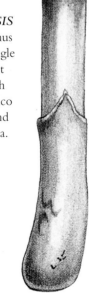

Aerial, club-shaped inflorescence

HELOSIS CAYENNENSIS
The *Helosis* genus contains this single species of root parasite, which occurs in Mexico and Central and South America.

Inflorescence and tuber

BALANOPHORA INVOLUCRATA
The *Balanophora* genus contains 15 species of root parasites, native to the Old World tropics.

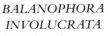

BIRCHES, CATALPAS, AND TRUMPET VINES

The Betulaceae family of medium-sized wind-pollinated trees and shrubs includes the alders (*Alnus*), birches (*Betula*), hazels (*Corylus*), and hornbeams (*Carpinus*). They bear simple, alternate, deciduous leaves and unisexual clusters of flowers that include pendulous catkins. The fruit is a single-seeded nut, often winged for wind dispersal. Mostly tropical or subtropical, the tropical vines (Bignoniaceae) include the jacarandas, catalpas, and trumpet vines.

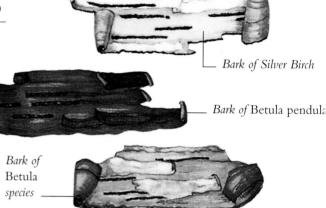

Bark of Silver Birch

Bark of *Betula pendula*

Bark of *Betula species*

BIRCH
Betula species
Birch trees have smooth bark exfoliating in large, thin layers, and provide valuable hardwood timbers.

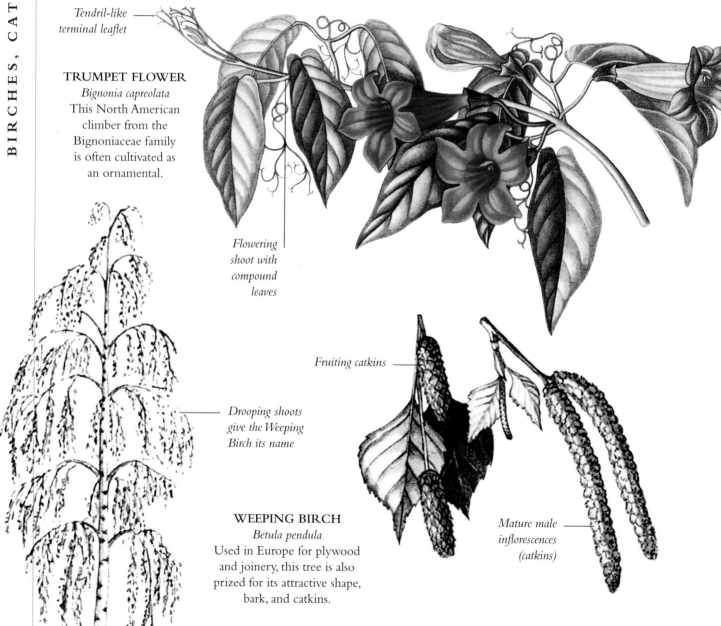

Tendril-like terminal leaflet

TRUMPET FLOWER
Bignonia capreolata
This North American climber from the Bignoniaceae family is often cultivated as an ornamental.

Flowering shoot with compound leaves

Drooping shoots give the Weeping Birch its name

Fruiting catkins

WEEPING BIRCH
Betula pendula
Used in Europe for plywood and joinery, this tree is also prized for its attractive shape, bark, and catkins.

Mature male inflorescences (catkins)

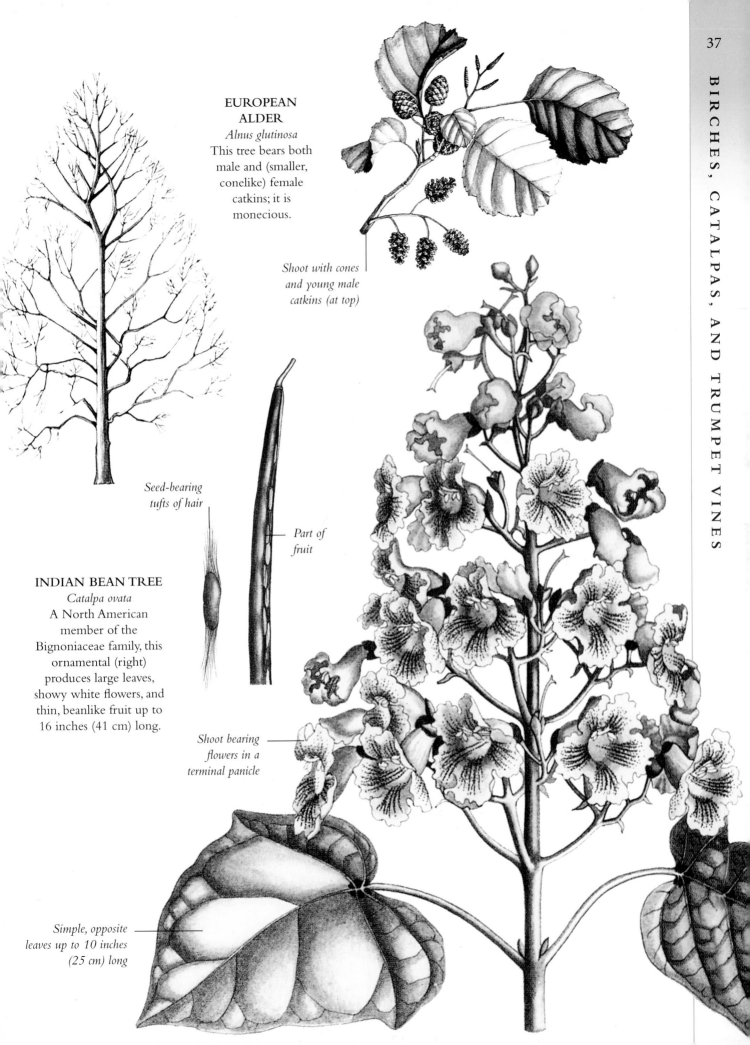

EUROPEAN ALDER
Alnus glutinosa
This tree bears both male and (smaller, conelike) female catkins; it is monecious.

Shoot with cones and young male catkins (at top)

Seed-bearing tufts of hair

Part of fruit

INDIAN BEAN TREE
Catalpa ovata
A North American member of the Bignoniaceae family, this ornamental (right) produces large leaves, showy white flowers, and thin, beanlike fruit up to 16 inches (41 cm) long.

Shoot bearing flowers in a terminal panicle

Simple, opposite leaves up to 10 inches (25 cm) long

BORAGES AND ANNATTOS

Borages and forget-me-nots (Boraginaceae) range from large trees to small annual herbs. They grow worldwide in a wide variety of habitats. The leaves can be alternate or opposite, rarely with serrated edges. Annattos (Bixaceae) are shrubs native to South America.

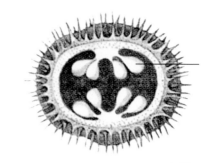

Cross section of
Lipstick Tree ovary,
showing ovules

Section of fruit
with numerous
red seeds

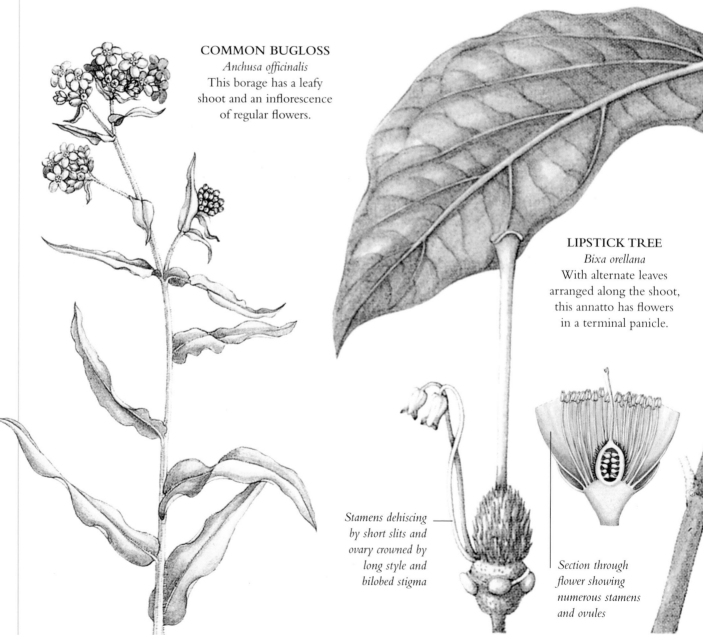

COMMON BUGLOSS
Anchusa officinalis
This borage has a leafy
shoot and an inflorescence
of regular flowers.

LIPSTICK TREE
Bixa orellana
With alternate leaves
arranged along the shoot,
this annatto has flowers
in a terminal panicle.

Stamens dehiscing
by short slits and
ovary crowned by
long style and
bilobed stigma

Section through
flower showing
numerous stamens
and ovules

Honeywort
corolla opened

Calyx and
four-lobed
gynoecium

HONEYWORT
Cerinthe major
This borage features a leafy shoot and
inflorescence, as well as a four-lobed
gynoecium, arising from the base of
the ovary between the lobes.

COMMON
VIPER'S BUGLOSS
Echium vulgare
This borage has an
inflorescence of irregular
flowers and a four-lobed ovary.

BRASSICAS

A cosmopolitan, mainly herbaceous family,
brassicas (Brassicaceae) can often be
recognized by their four-petalled, cross-
shaped (cruciform) flowers and the
astringent, mustard taste of the leaves.
Most species grow around the
Mediterranean basin. Many
are valuable agricultural
crops, such as mustard,
cress, cabbage, turnip,
and oilseed rape.

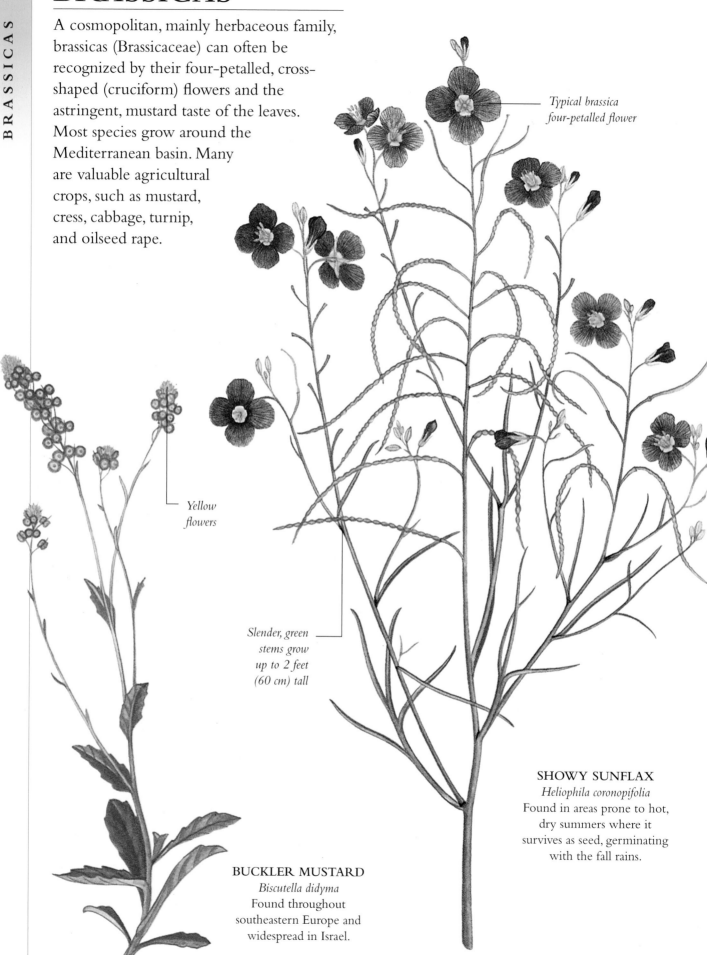

*Typical brassica
four-petalled flower*

*Yellow
flowers*

*Slender, green
stems grow
up to 2 feet
(60 cm) tall*

SHOWY SUNFLAX
Heliophila coronopifolia
Found in areas prone to hot,
dry summers where it
survives as seed, germinating
with the fall rains.

BUCKLER MUSTARD
Biscutella didyma
Found throughout
southeastern Europe and
widespread in Israel.

CANDYTUFT
Iberis pinnata
Commonly used as an
ornamental garden plant.

*Outer petals
longer than
inner petals*

*Half flower
showing stamens
with long and
short filaments*

PURPLE MISTRESS
Moricandia arvensis
Common throughout the
temperate regions of the world,
this is now sometimes
cultivated as a garden plant.

*Lush leaves
grow in moist
environments*

BUDDLEJAS, FRANKINCENSE, AND MYRRH

Buddlejas (Buddlejaceae) are shrubs, trees, and woody climbers from tropical and subtropical regions. They are popular ornamental plants, commonly called "butterfly bushes" for the fact that they attract nectaring butterflies. The tropical trees and shrubs in the Burseraceae family (which include frankincense and myrrh) have more practical uses—providing the aromatic resins used in incense, perfumes, and soaps.

PAPERBARK CORK
Commiphora marlothii
A native of Zimbabwe, this plant is named for the way the old bark peels off in sheets to reveal new, green bark beneath.

Terminal fruit cluster

Canarium hirtellum *flower*

Flower with perianth removed to show stamens

Section of ovary

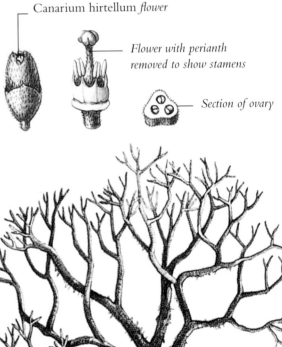

Boswellia papyrifera *habit*

INCENSE TREE
Protium guianense
One of many species referred to as incense trees, the sap is dried and ground and then burns fragrantly.

FRANKINCENSE TREE
Boswellia papyrifera
Native to East Africa and now regarded as endangered, this tree is the source of the famous frankincense resin.

— *Fruit*

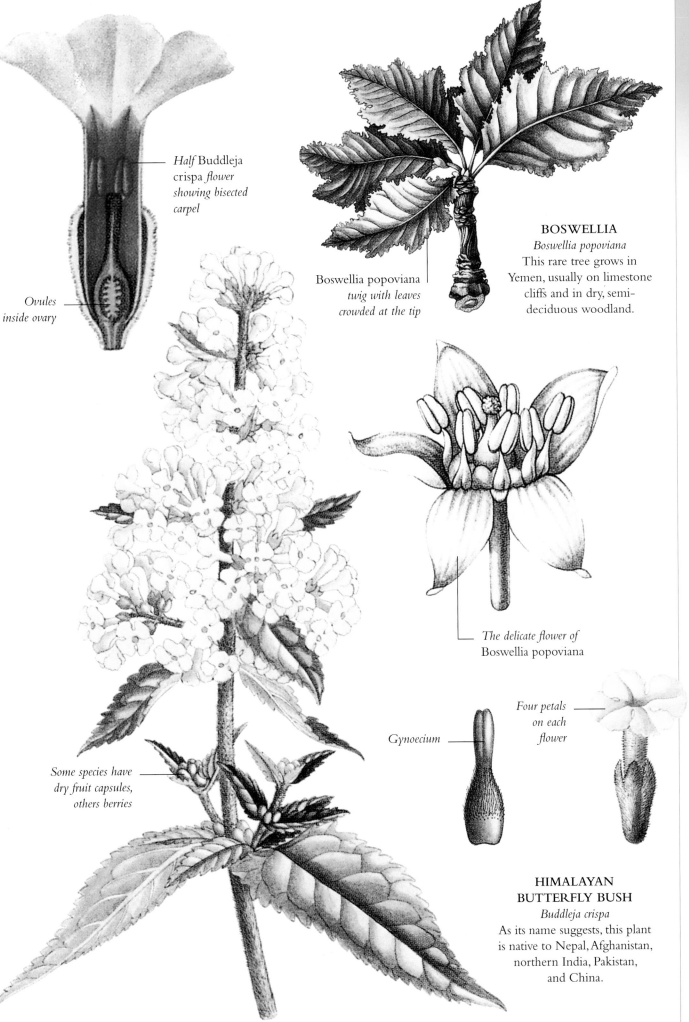

Half Buddleja crispa *flower showing bisected carpel*

Ovules inside ovary

BOSWELLIA

Boswellia popoviana
This rare tree grows in Yemen, usually on limestone cliffs and in dry, semi-deciduous woodland.

Boswellia popoviana *twig with leaves crowded at the tip*

The delicate flower of Boswellia popoviana

Some species have dry fruit capsules, others berries

Gynoecium

Four petals on each flower

HIMALAYAN BUTTERFLY BUSH

Buddleja crispa
As its name suggests, this plant is native to Nepal, Afghanistan, northern India, Pakistan, and China.

CACTI

These trees, shrubs, and climbers, which make up the family Cactaceae, can generally be recognized by their leafless appearance and profusion of spines. They are predominantly plants of the semideserts and warmer parts of North and South America and can also be found on other continents. The fruit of some cacti can be eaten raw or made into jams or syrups, and *Opuntia* species (prickly pears) are grown commercially in parts of Mexico and California.

CACTUS APPLE
Opuntia engelmannii
This cactus, native to Mexico and the southern United States, has a many-jointed, disklike stem.

The fine spines, or glochids, are easily detached

SAGUARO
Carnegiea gigantea
Native to Arizona and California in the United States, Saguaros grow up to 45 feet (13.7 m) tall.

Multi-branched candelabra habit and ribbed stems

ROSE PINCUSHION
Mammillaria zeilmanniana
A dwarf cactus found in the deserts of Mexico.

Flowers arise from base of tubercles

Solitary stem of spirally arranged tubercles

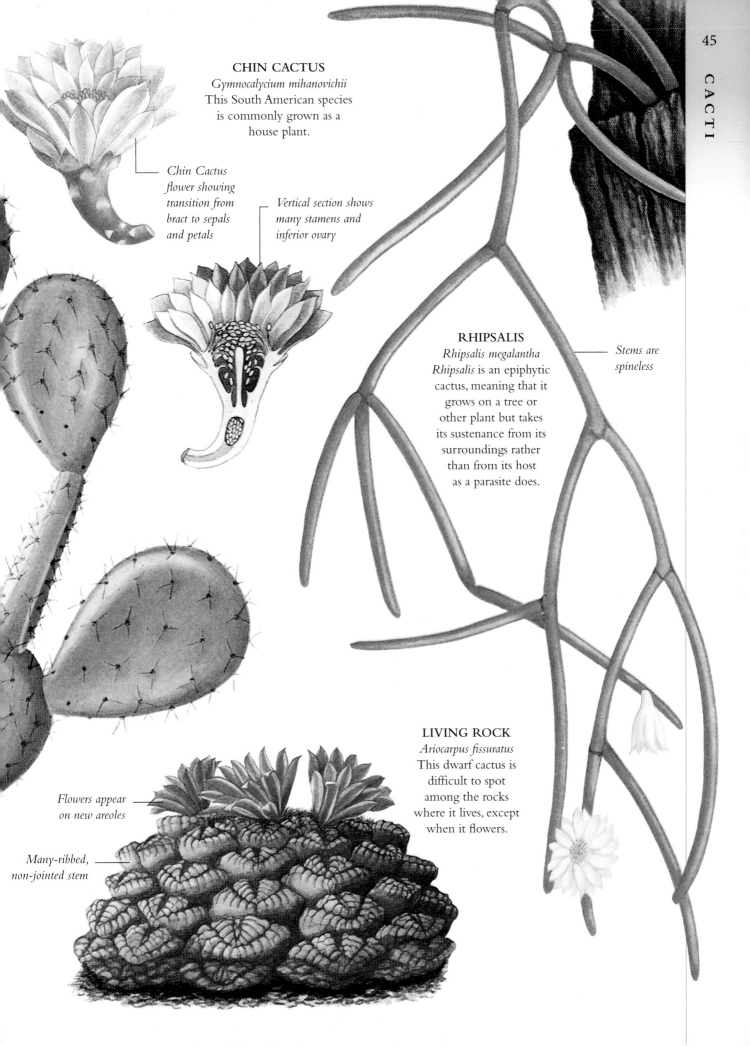

CHIN CACTUS
Gymnocalycium mihanovichii
This South American species
is commonly grown as a
house plant.

*Chin Cactus
flower showing
transition from
bract to sepals
and petals*

*Vertical section shows
many stamens and
inferior ovary*

RHIPSALIS
Rhipsalis megalantha
Rhipsalis is an epiphytic
cactus, meaning that it
grows on a tree or
other plant but takes
its sustenance from its
surroundings rather
than from its host
as a parasite does.

*Stems are
spineless*

LIVING ROCK
Ariocarpus fissuratus
This dwarf cactus is
difficult to spot
among the rocks
where it lives, except
when it flowers.

*Flowers appear
on new areoles*

*Many-ribbed,
non-jointed stem*

BELLFLOWERS AND LOBELIAS

There are nearly 2,400 species of bellflowers and lobelias (Campanulaceae). These plants have a near-cosmopolitan distribution, with a particularly rich diversity in South Africa. They are only absent from Antarctica, the Sahara Desert, northeast Asia, and northern Greenland. Many species are cultivated as garden plants, and certain *Lobelia* species have been used to tackle nicotine addiction.

CANARINA
Canarina eminii
Canarinas grow mainly in East Africa, although the genus is named for a species (*Canarina canariensis*) native to the Canary Islands.

Leaves grow as opposites on stem

Axillary, regular flowers

TRACHELIUM
Trachelium rumenlianum
The shoots of this plant have alternate leaves and terminal inflorescences.

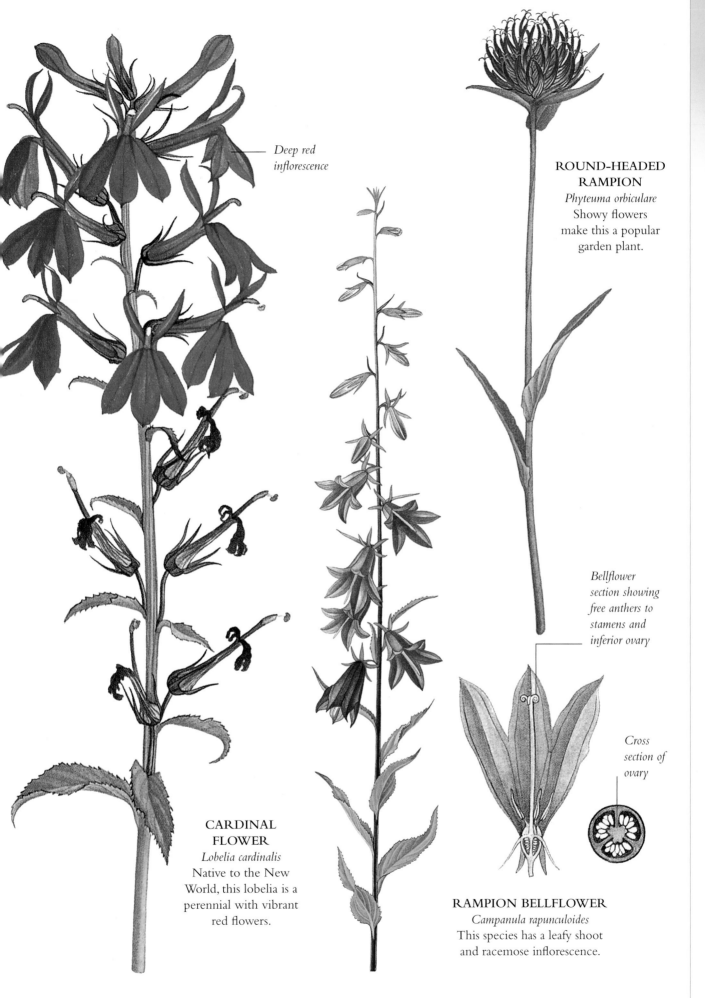

*Deep red
inflorescence*

**ROUND-HEADED
RAMPION**
Phyteuma orbiculare
Showy flowers
make this a popular
garden plant.

*Bellflower
section showing
free anthers to
stamens and
inferior ovary*

*Cross
section of
ovary*

**CARDINAL
FLOWER**
Lobelia cardinalis
Native to the New
World, this lobelia is a
perennial with vibrant
red flowers.

RAMPION BELLFLOWER
Campanula rapunculoides
This species has a leafy shoot
and racemose inflorescence.

CARNATIONS

Carnations (Caryophyllaceae) grow in most regions, although by far the greatest concentration is in the Mediterranean Basin and in adjacent regions of Europe and southwestern Asia. Some, notably species in the genus *Dianthus*, are easily recognized as ornamental garden plants and are also cultivated for the cut-flower market.

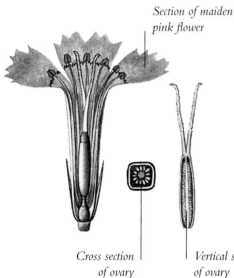

Section of maiden pink flower

Cross section of ovary

Vertical section of ovary

MAIDEN PINK
Dianthus deltoides
The Maiden Pink produces flowers with fused sepals, deeply notched petals, twice as many stamens as petals, and a superior ovary crowned by two styles.

Telephium *flower*

TELEPHIUM
Telephium imperati
Telephium develops flowers with five sepals, five petals, five stamens, and three styles.

GRASSLEAF STARWORT
Stellaria graminea
As pictured here,
this starwort displays
swollen nodes and
cymose inflorescences.

*Deeply
notched
petals*

RED CAMPION
Silene dioica
The Red Campion has
flowers with a deeply
cleft limb on each petal.

*Leaves grow
as opposites*

SANDWORT
Arenaria purpurascens
Like most of the larger
carnations, the *Arenaria*
species are native to
the Northern
Hemisphere.

SPINDLE TREES AND ROCKROSES

Spindle trees (Celastraceae) are shrubs, trees, or woody climbers with a pronounced floral disk and often a characteristic capsule. They are found in the tropics and subtropics. Extracts from some species have been used to make medicines, and in some regions the bark has been used to make poison for arrow tips. Rockroses (Cistaceae) grow in the warm-temperate zone, especially in southern Europe.

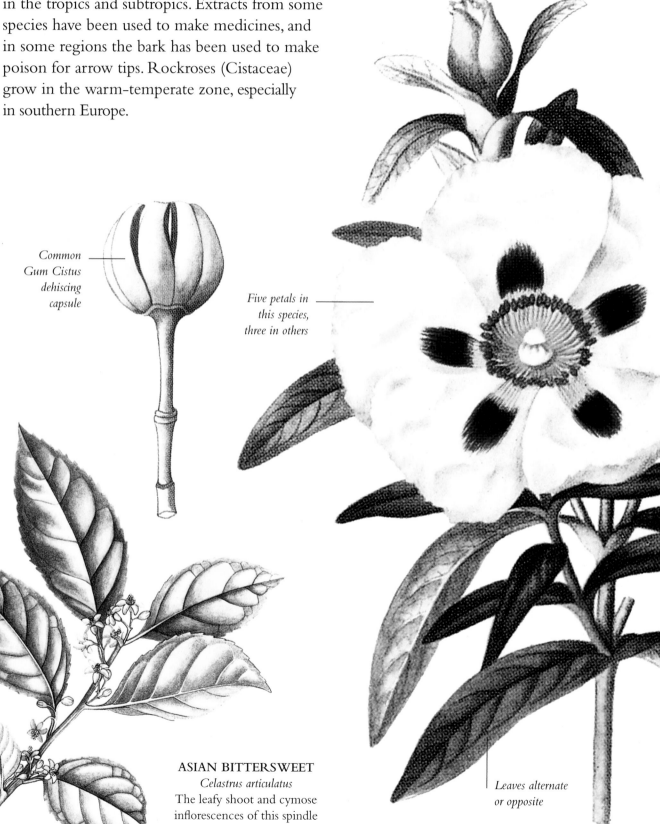

COMMON GUM CISTUS
Cistus ladanifer
This rockrose species is the source of the aromatic ladanum gum used commercially in the perfume industry.

Common Gum Cistus dehiscing capsule

Five petals in this species, three in others

ASIAN BITTERSWEET
Celastrus articulatus
The leafy shoot and cymose inflorescences of this spindle tree are shown here.

Leaves alternate or opposite

*Seed and
seed cover*

Dehiscing fruit

HIPPOCRATEA

Hippocratea welwitschii
There are about 100 species
of *Hippocratea*, a genus of
spindle tree found mainly
in the tropics, especially
West Africa.

SPINDLE TREE

Euonymus myrianthus
Native to western China, this
spindle tree is shown bearing
capsule-shaped fruits.

*Flower with four
distinct petals on
a fleshy disk*

Flower stamen

GARCINIAS AND COCHLOSPERMS

The pantropical family Clusiaceae is made up of more than 1,600 species of trees and shrubs, including the garcinias and Chewstick. The less widespread cochlosperms (Cochlospermaceae) are native to tropical America and Africa. The Albany Pitcher Plant—the only species in the family Cephalotaceae—is endemic to Australia. It is a carnivorous herb that traps unwary insects, deriving sustenance from their decomposing bodies.

ALBANY PITCHER PLANT
Cephalotus follicularis
This carnivorous evergreen herb is native to southwestern Australia.

Leafless stalk to inflorescence

Albany Pitcher Plant pitcher lid closes to trap insects

Leaves form a pitcher 1–2 inches (2.5–5 cm) tall and half filled with water

Half flower showing stamens in bundles

AARON'S BEARD
Hypericum calycinum
Aaron's Beard has decussate leaves and a solitary, terminal flower.

CHEWSTICK
Symphonia globulifera
Shoots of the Chewstick have
terminal inflorescence and
produce berry fruit.

**ALEXANDRIAN
LAUREL**
Calophyllum inophyllum
Drugs and dyes have been
produced from the bark of
this tropical plant.

*Inflorescences
grow in axils of
terminal leaves*

COCHLOSPERMUM
Cochlospermum tinctorium
A woody shrub with
large flowers, this has
been used to produce
medicines in Africa.

*Flowers are
hermaphroditic*

MORNING GLORIES, BINDWEEDS, AND GOURDS

Morning glories and bindweeds (Convolvulaceae) are common throughout tropical and temperate regions. While some pose a problem as agricultural and garden weeds, others are cultivated as ornamentals, and Sweet Potato *(Ipomoea batatas)* is an important commercial crop. The gourd or pumpkin family (Cucurbitaceae) includes some major food crops, including squashes, pumpkins, gourds, marrows, cucumbers, and melons.

Flowers are star-shaped, or actinomorphic

IVY GOURD
Coccinea grandis
Here showing leaves, female flowers, and tendrils as well as ripe and unripe fruit

Young Jiaogulan fruit with remains of styles

JIAOGULAN
Gynostemma pentaphyllum
Growing wild in China, this plant has long been used to make a medicinal tea.

ZANONIA
Zanonia indica
This is a medium-sized liana growing in South Asia.

Sechium edule stamens partly joined in single column

Sechium edule *female flower with discoid stigma*

Female flower

CHAYOTE
Sechium edule
The vine on which the fruit grows can reach up to 39 feet (11.9 m) high.

Tendrils grasp surfaces to aid climbing

TRICHOSANTHES
Trichosanthes tricuspidata
This species displays large, palmately lobed leaves.

PURPLE MORNING GLORY
Ipomoea purpurea
A native of Central America, the flower of *Ipomoea purpurea* is shown here with the corolla opened out to show stamens inserted at the base.

Female flower with petals and sepals removed

Male flower

Ripe fruit turns from green to red

CROOKNECK SQUASH
Cucurbita moschata
Some species of *Cucurbita*, including this, are pollinated by specialized squash bees, and some, in South America, by bats.

LIGHTWOODS, CYTINUS, AND LEATHERWOOD

The lightwoods (Cunoniaceae) are evergreen trees and shrubs native to the Southern Hemisphere. The wood of some is used in the construction industry. Leatherwood (Cyrillaceae) has attractive fruit, flowers, and foliage and is grown as an ornamental. The *Cytinus* species (Cytinaceae) are very different: they are root parasites growing in South Africa, on the island of Madagascar, and around the Mediterreanean Sea.

Davidsonia pruriens *fruit*

Inflorescences in branched raceme or panicle

WEINMANNIA
Weinmannia hildebrandtii
Here showing its characteristic trifoliate leaves and flowers in panicles

Weinmannia hildebrandtii *flower*

BUTTERKNIFE TREE
Cunonia capensis
The Butterknife Tree is one of the lightwoods. It has serrate palmate leaves and flowers in a panicle.

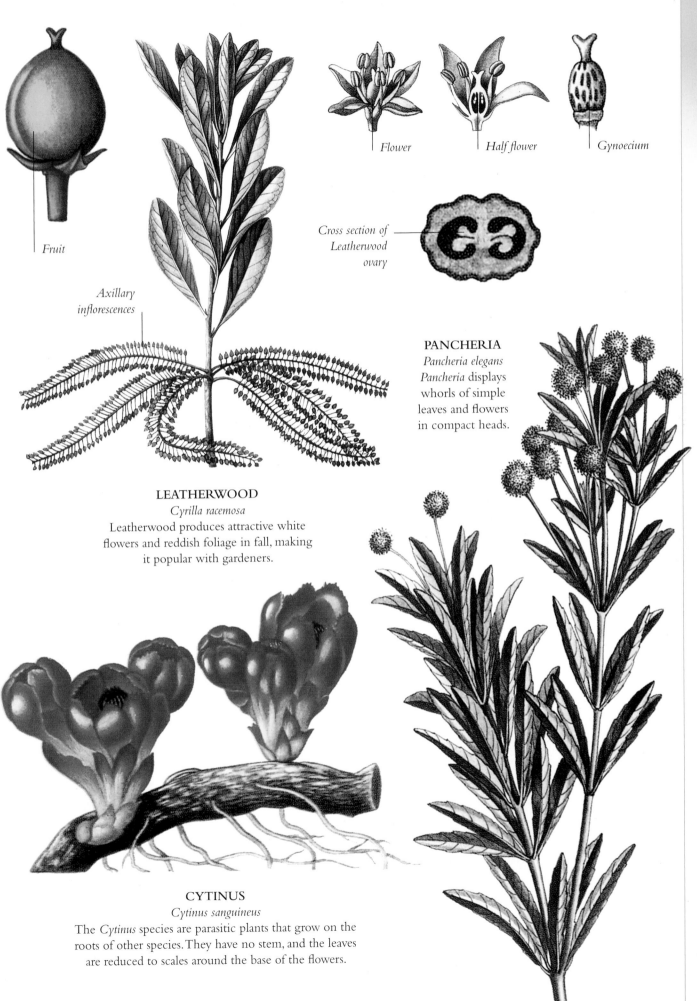

Fruit

Flower

Half flower

Gynoecium

Axillary
inflorescences

Cross section of
Leatherwood
ovary

PANCHERIA
Pancheria elegans
Pancheria displays
whorls of simple
leaves and flowers
in compact heads.

LEATHERWOOD
Cyrilla racemosa
Leatherwood produces attractive white
flowers and reddish foliage in fall, making
it popular with gardeners.

CYTINUS
Cytinus sanguineus
The *Cytinus* species are parasitic plants that grow on the
roots of other species. They have no stem, and the leaves
are reduced to scales around the base of the flowers.

DILLENIAS, SCABIOUS, AND TEASELS

The dillenias (Dilleniaceae) form a large family of medium-sized tropical trees and shrubs that grow in lowland forests or on savannas. Some species, such as *Hibbertia scandens* and *Dillenia indica,* are occasionally grown as ornamentals, while the wood of some *Dillenia* species is used for general construction and boatbuilding. The scabious and teasels (Dipsacaceae) are annual or perennial herbs or low shrubs, and they are noted for their striking inflorescences.

Inflorescence is a terminal compact flower head

PTEROCEPHALUS
Pterocephalus perennis
Often cultivated as a rock-garden plant, this species grows mainly in the Mediterranean region.

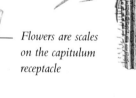

Flowers are scales on the capitulum receptacle

Flower head surrounded by spiny bracts

Flowering shoot

FULLER'S TEASEL
Dipsacus fullonum
The inflorescences of this species were formerly used for raising the nap on cloth.

SCABIOSA
Scabiosa anthemifolia
This species' range extends from the Mediterranean to South Africa, and even, sparsely, to Japan.

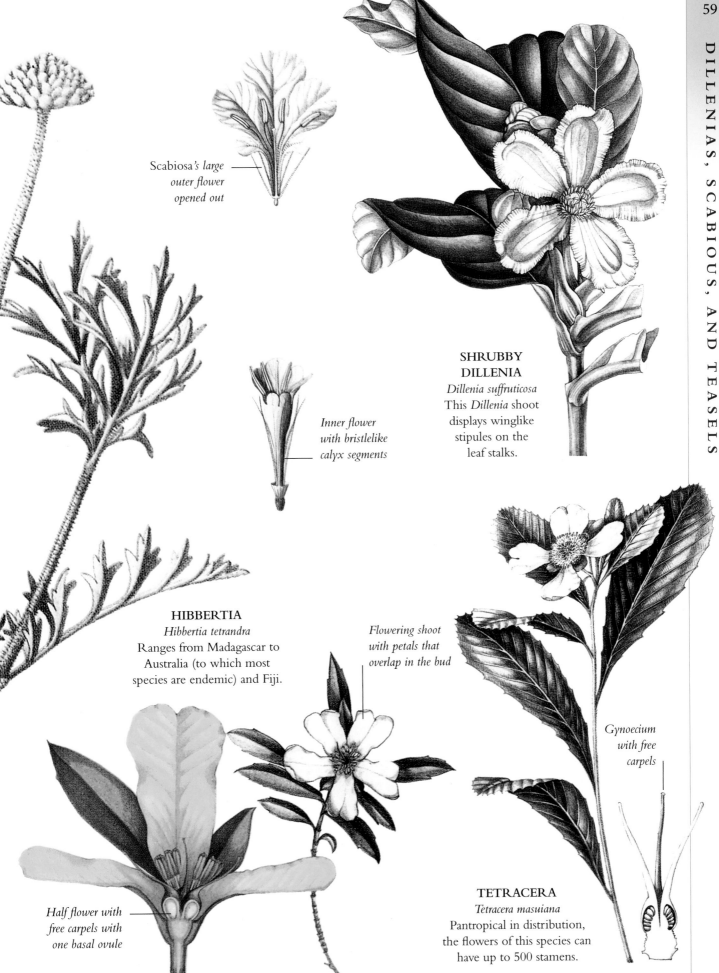

Scabiosa's large
outer flower
opened out

**SHRUBBY
DILLENIA**
Dillenia suffruticosa
This *Dillenia* shoot
displays winglike
stipules on the
leaf stalks.

Inner flower
with bristlelike
calyx segments

HIBBERTIA
Hibbertia tetrandra
Ranges from Madagascar to
Australia (to which most
species are endemic) and Fiji.

Flowering shoot
with petals that
overlap in the bud

Gynoecium
with free
carpels

Half flower with
free carpels with
one basal ovule

TETRACERA
Tetracera masuiana
Pantropical in distribution,
the flowers of this species can
have up to 500 stamens.

SUNDEWS AND DURIANS

The sundews (Droseraceae) are carnivorous plants. They have colonized a wide variety of habitats, from fully aquatic to seasonally dry. The Venus Flytrap uses a trap to catch its prey, while the Cape Sundew rolls insects in its sticky leaves. The durians (Durionaceae) are cultivated throughout Southeast Asia for their seed arils (covers).

Perianth opened out to reveal stamens

Half section of ovary

Gynoecium

Sticky stalked glands on leaves

CAPE SUNDEW
Drosera capensis
The Cape Sundew has a basal rosette of leaves covered in stalked glands, which secrete a sticky mucus to trap insects.

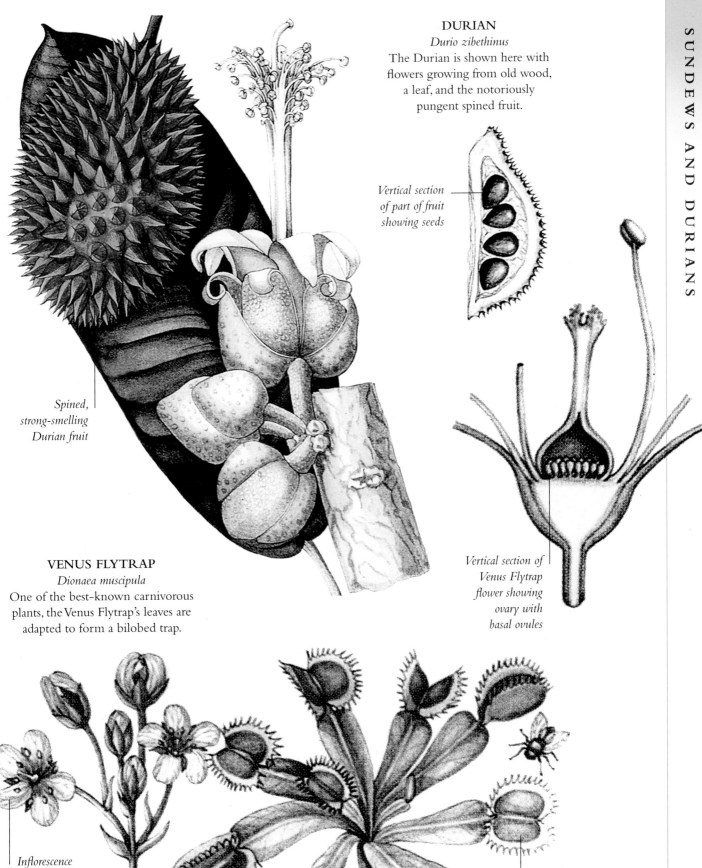

DURIAN
Durio zibethinus
The Durian is shown here with flowers growing from old wood, a leaf, and the notoriously pungent spined fruit.

Vertical section of part of fruit showing seeds

Spined, strong-smelling Durian fruit

Vertical section of Venus Flytrap flower showing ovary with basal ovules

VENUS FLYTRAP
Dionaea muscipula
One of the best-known carnivorous plants, the Venus Flytrap's leaves are adapted to form a bilobed trap.

Inflorescence

Hinged trap catches insects

HEATHERS AND RHODODENDRONS

The heathers and rhododendrons (Ericaceae) make up a large family of flowering plants, whose representatives are found in most regions of the world. They include the genera *Erica*, *Rhododendron*, and *Gaultheria* (wintergreens). Most are shrubs or climbers, though there are also herbaceous examples. The leaves are always simple and without stipules, usually alternate, and often evergreen.

AGAPETES
Agapetes macrantha
There are more than 400 subspecies of this climbing shrub in Southeast Asia.

Half flower

Axillary inflorescence

SNOW PLANT
Sarcodes sanguinea
This is a parasitic plant of conifer forests in North America.

Stamens are free or rarely attached to the petals

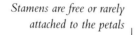

YUNNAN RHODODENDRON
Rhododendron yunnanense
This plant produces a highly toxic honey, which is fatal in large doses.

Petals are fused, apart from pointed tips

HEATHER SPECIES
Erica vallis-aranearum
Grows near the southwest coast of South Africa, where about 450 *Erica* species can be found.

RED CROWBERRY
Empetrum rubrum
Grows solitary flowers in
leaf axils; produces
drupaceous fruit

*Narrow
ericoid needles*

*Three
perianth
segments*

*Gynoecium with lobed
ovary and stigma*

TRAILING ARBUTUS
Epigaea repens
An evergreen shrub with
pink flowers, fading to
nearly white

WINTERGREEN
Gaultheria species
These shrubs have racemose
inflorescences, usually urn-shaped,
and stamens with swollen filaments.

OUTENIQUA HEATH
Erica versicolor var. *costata*
A colorful plant with
terminal racemes with
paired bracteoles.

Gaultheria
berry

SPURGES AND OLEASTERS

The spurges (Euphorbiaceae) are a diverse group of ornamental trees, shrubs, herbs, and climbers, with some important commercial crops such as cassavas, Rubber Tree, and Castor Oil Plant. Oleasters (Elaeagnaceae) are a much smaller group, some species of which produce edible fruits.

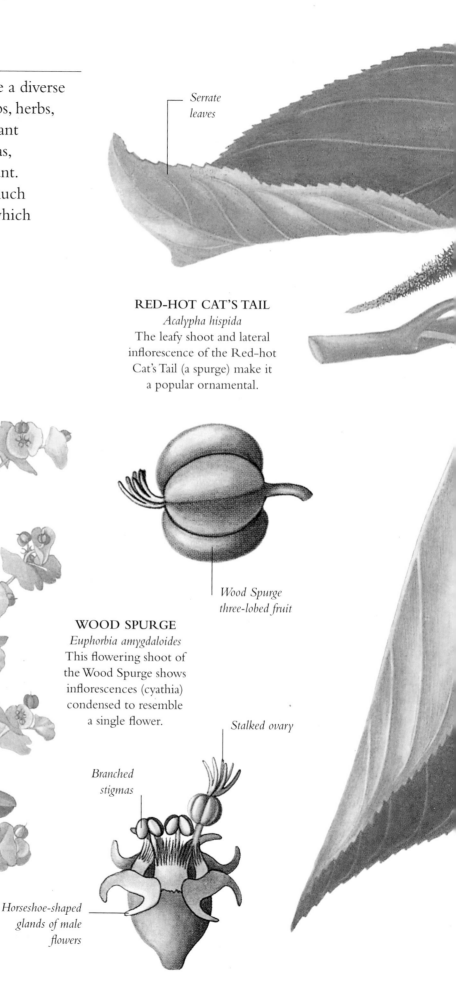

Serrate leaves

RED-HOT CAT'S TAIL
Acalypha hispida
The leafy shoot and lateral inflorescence of the Red-hot Cat's Tail (a spurge) make it a popular ornamental.

Wood Spurge three-lobed fruit

WOOD SPURGE
Euphorbia amygdaloides
This flowering shoot of the Wood Spurge shows inflorescences (cyathia) condensed to resemble a single flower.

Stalked ovary

Branched stigmas

Horseshoe-shaped glands of male flowers

CHERRY ELAEAGNUS
Elaeagnus multiflora
The shoot shown here bears the fleshy fruits for which the plant is named.

Alternate, leathery leaves

EUPHORBIA STAPFII
This cactuslike plant is a member of the vast spurge family.

Croton fruit

CROTON
Croton fothergillifolius
Croton is shown here as a characteristic leafy shoot with flowers and fruit.

BEECHES, OAKS, AND SWEET CHESTNUTS

A commercially important family (Fagaceae) of deciduous or evergreen hardwood trees (more rarely shrubs with edible fruits, and ornamentals), these species have a colossal total mass, and have a long fossil record, stretching back over 90 million years. It is the source of the world's most important temperate hardwoods, particularly oak, beech, and chestnut. Many species of chestnut, but principally the sweet chestnut, also produce large edible nuts.

HOLLY OAK
Quercus ilex
Male flowers cluster in pendulous catkins with female flowers at the bases.

Entire leaf margin

ENGLISH OAK
Quercus robur
This species is deciduous, shedding its lobed leaves and stipules annually.

EUROPEAN BEECH
Fagus sylvatica
A deciduous tree with simple, alternate leaves.

Quercus robur
leafless tree

Fagus sylvatica
leafless tree

Remains of male catkin

Closed spiny cupule

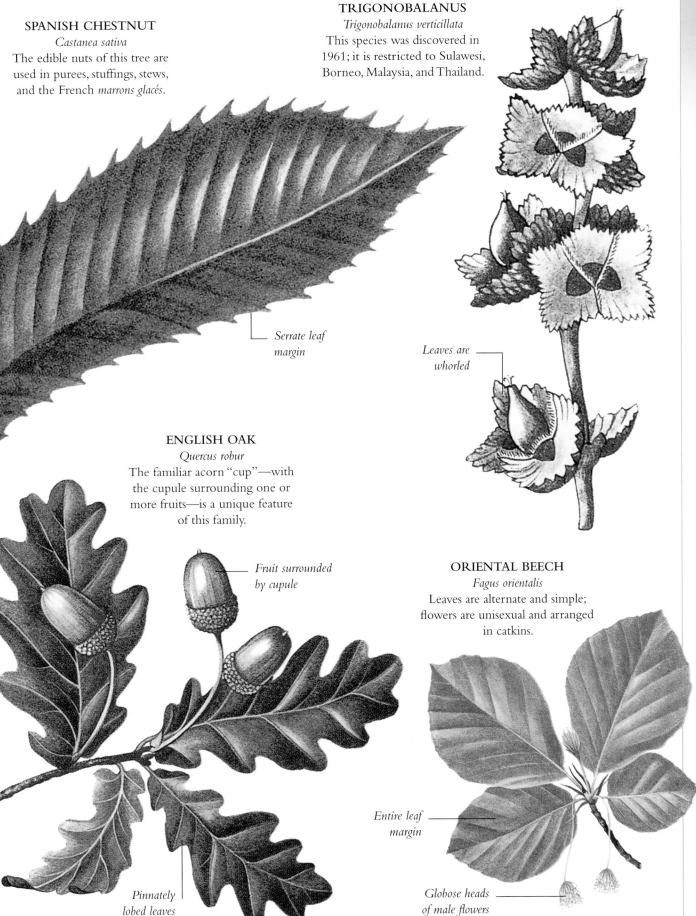

SPANISH CHESTNUT
Castanea sativa
The edible nuts of this tree are
used in purees, stuffings, stews,
and the French *marrons glacés*.

TRIGONOBALANUS
Trigonobalanus verticillata
This species was discovered in
1961; it is restricted to Sulawesi,
Borneo, Malaysia, and Thailand.

*Serrate leaf
margin*

*Leaves are
whorled*

ENGLISH OAK
Quercus robur
The familiar acorn "cup"—with
the cupule surrounding one or
more fruits—is a unique feature
of this family.

*Fruit surrounded
by cupule*

ORIENTAL BEECH
Fagus orientalis
Leaves are alternate and simple;
flowers are unisexual and arranged
in catkins.

*Entire leaf
margin*

*Pinnately
lobed leaves*

*Globose heads
of male flowers*

GENTIANS, IDESIA, AND FRANKENIAS

There are more than 1,600 species of gentians (Gentianaceae). Although most are small, annual to perennial herbs, some tropical species can grow up to 115 feet (35 m) high. The Idesia, a deciduous tree native to East Asia, is a species in the family Salicaceae; it is cultivated as an ornamental and produces edible berries. Frankenias (Frankeniaceae) generally grow in coastal regions with a Mediterranean climate. They are clump-forming shrubs or cushionlike shrubs with a pronounced salt and gypsum tolerance as well as stems with salt glands.

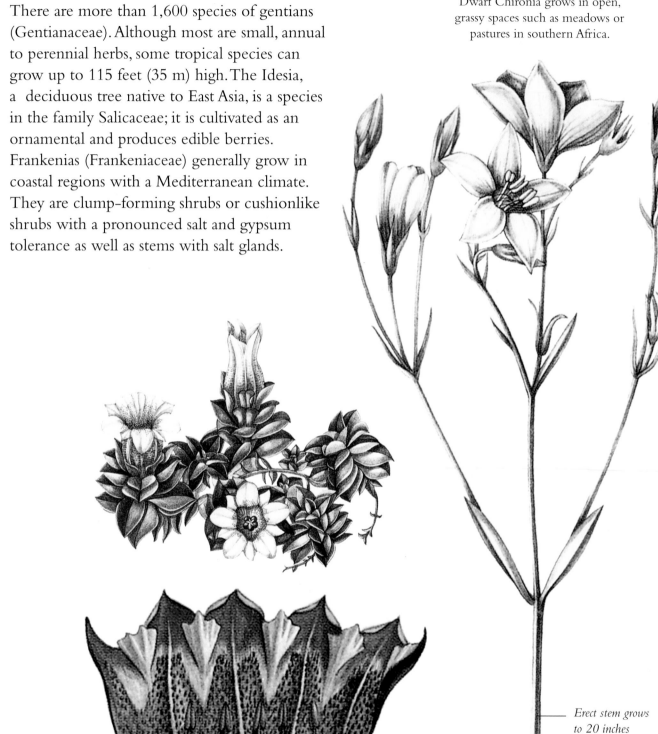

DWARF CHIRONIA
Chironia purpurascens
Dwarf Chironia grows in open, grassy spaces such as meadows or pastures in southern Africa.

Erect stem grows to 20 inches (50 cm) tall

GENTIAN
Gentiana depressa
This gentian is displaying its leafy shoots and terminal inflorescences with funnel-shaped corollae.

Corolla opened out

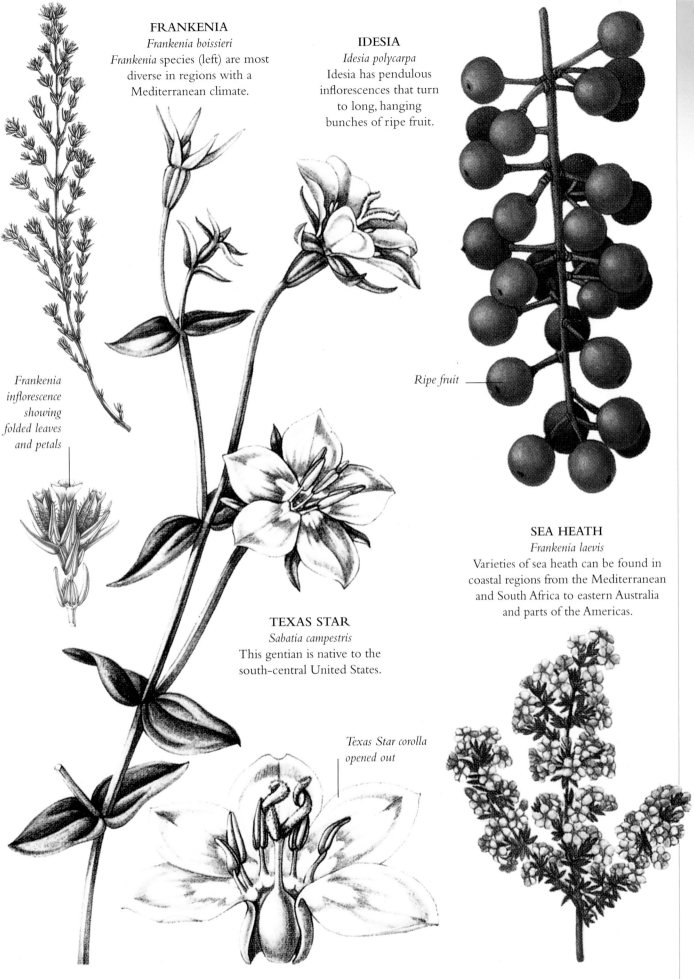

FRANKENIA
Frankenia boissieri
Frankenia species (left) are most
diverse in regions with a
Mediterranean climate.

IDESIA
Idesia polycarpa
Idesia has pendulous
inflorescences that turn
to long, hanging
bunches of ripe fruit.

*Frankenia
inflorescence
showing
folded leaves
and petals*

Ripe fruit —

SEA HEATH
Frankenia laevis
Varieties of sea heath can be found in
coastal regions from the Mediterranean
and South Africa to eastern Australia
and parts of the Americas.

TEXAS STAR
Sabatia campestris
This gentian is native to the
south-central United States.

*Texas Star corolla
opened out*

GERANIUMS, LIQUIDAMBARS, AND WITCH HAZELS

The geraniums (Geraniaceae) are widely distributed herbs or shrubs. Some are of major horticultural importance for their colorful flowers. Witch hazels and liquidambars (Hamamelidaceae) are temperate to tropical trees and shrubs, useful for both their high-quality timber (*Altingia, Liquidambar*) and gums with medicinal properties (*Liquidambar, Hamamelis*).

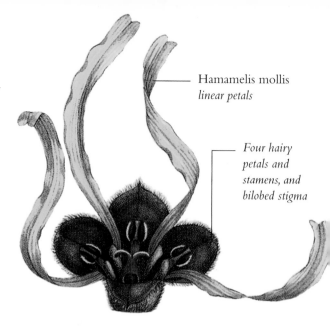

Hamamelis mollis linear petals

Four hairy petals and stamens, and bilobed stigma

Geranium malviflorum *bilobed petals*

ROMAN CRANESBILL
Erodium romanum
This geranium speices is native to the Mediterranean region.

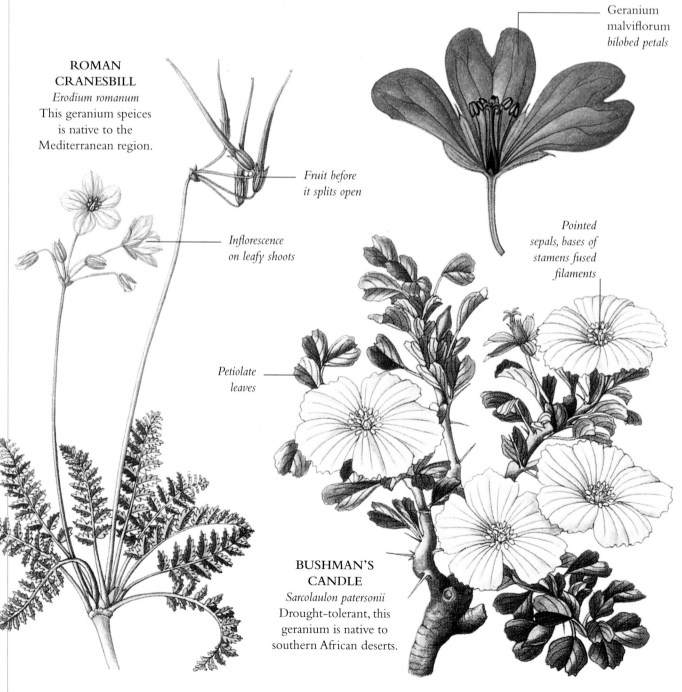

Fruit before it splits open

Inflorescence on leafy shoots

Pointed sepals, bases of stamens fused filaments

Petiolate leaves

BUSHMAN'S CANDLE
Sarcolaulon patersonii
Drought-tolerant, this geranium is native to southern African deserts.

HONG KONG ROSE

Rhodoleia championii
This species bears
alternate, ovate leaves
and symmetrical flowers.

CHINESE WITCH HAZEL

Hamamelis mollis
Native to temperate East
Asia, this species is widely
kept as an ornamental

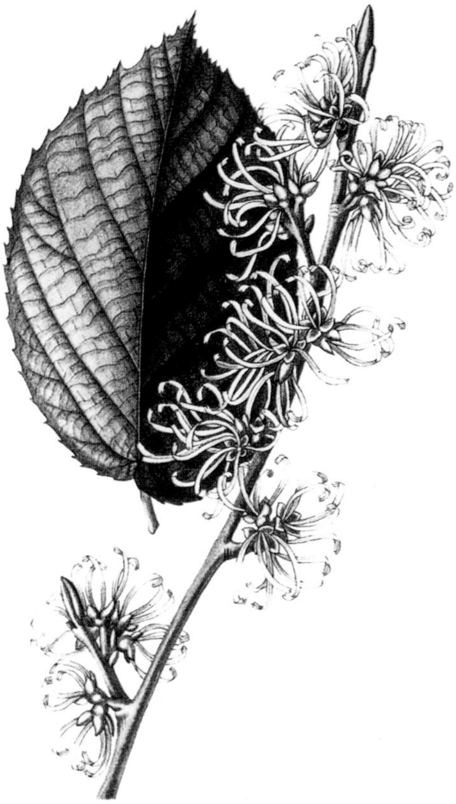

Flowered capitula
with numerous
surrounding bracts

Inflorescence
massed into
dense head

Dehisced
fruit

MOUNTAIN WITCH ALDER

Fothergilla major
Often grown as an
ornamental, this
species bears early
sweet-scented flowers.

Cross section
of ovary

Bicarpolate
gynoecium

Ripe
fruits

AFRICAN VIOLETS AND GLOXINIAS

Although mostly tropical herbs and shrubs, this family (Gesneriaceae) also includes lianas and trees, and extends into southern temperate regions. Family members live from sea level to high alpine environments in the Himalayas and Andes. Most species prefer a moist situation but some, like the Pyrenean Violet, thrive in a rocky habitat.

Lipstick Plant half flower showing corolla tube constricted at the base

Yerba Parrera flower with part of calyx and corolla cut away

STREPTOCARPUS
Streptocarpus caulescens
This species of African violet displays a leafy shoot and deep purple flowers.

COLUMNEA
Columnea crassifolia
Columnea has alternate leaves and a solitary, two-lipped flower.

YERBA PARRERA
Gesneria cuneifolia
Yerba Parrera has a basal rosette of leaves with multiple pedicels bearing solitary flowers.

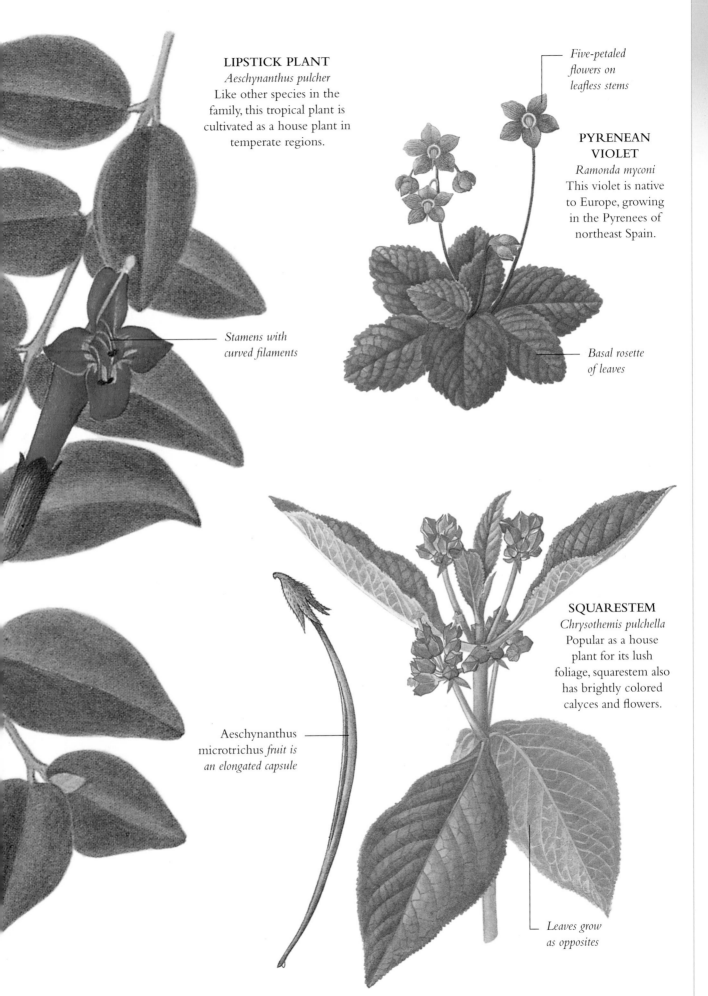

LIPSTICK PLANT
Aeschynanthus pulcher
Like other species in the
family, this tropical plant is
cultivated as a house plant in
temperate regions.

*Five-petaled
flowers on
leafless stems*

**PYRENEAN
VIOLET**
Ramonda myconi
This violet is native
to Europe, growing
in the Pyrenees of
northeast Spain.

*Stamens with
curved filaments*

*Basal rosette
of leaves*

SQUARESTEM
Chrysothemis pulchella
Popular as a house
plant for its lush
foliage, squarestem also
has brightly colored
calyces and flowers.

Aeschynanthus
microtrichus *fruit is
an elongated capsule*

*Leaves grow
as opposites*

PHACELIAS AND GUNNERAS

Phacelias (Hydrophyllaceae) are annual to perennial herbs and shrubs growing almost exclusively within the New World. Some genera have irritant hairs. Gunneras (Gunneraceae) are mostly rhizomatous or stoloniferous herbs, some of them gigantic, with rosettes of large leaves. Growing widely in the Southern Hemisphere, some are edible, and others are used in traditional medicine.

WILD CANTERBURY BELLS
Phacelia minor
An annual herb from the New World, with cincinnus inflorescences and irritant hairs.

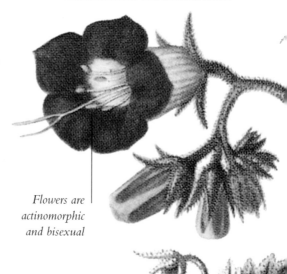

Flowers are actinomorphic and bisexual

Eastern Waterleaf dehiscing capsule with two seeds

Flowers in a headlike cyme

P. franklinii splitting capsule

Phacelia franklinii *cross section of ovary*

Phacelia tanacetifolia *half flower with appendages*

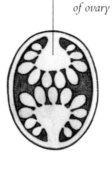

EASTERN WATERLEAF
Hydrophyllum virginianum
A perennial phacelia that bears pinnate leaves and cincinnus inflorescences

CHILEAN GUNNERA
Gunnera magellanica
Symbionic cyanobacteria live
in the rhizomes of this species.

*Funnel-shaped corolla
with five lobes*

*Leaves are alternate,
simple, and have
petioles*

Fruit

*Female
flower*

*Each male
flower
contains
two stamens*

*Tip of male
inflorescence*

ICACINACIAS
AND WALNUTS

Icacinacias (Icaninaceae) are small-
flowered shrubs, trees, and lianas that
grow in tropical forests. Parts of the plants
have been used locally to produce
treatments for ailments from rheumatism
to dysentery. Walnuts (Juglandaceae)
also grow in the tropics and are widely
cultivated in temperate regions, where
they are grown for their edible nuts
and the oil produced from them.

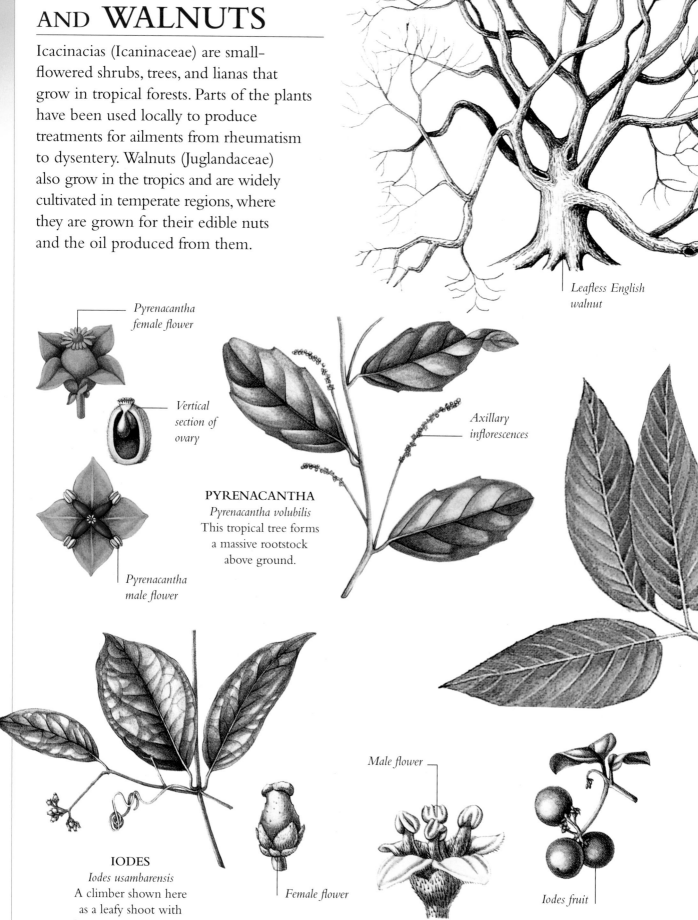

*Leafless English
walnut*

*Pyrenacantha
female flower*

*Vertical
section of
ovary*

*Axillary
inflorescences*

PYRENACANTHA
Pyrenacantha volubilis
This tropical tree forms
a massive rootstock
above ground.

*Pyrenacantha
male flower*

IODES
Iodes usambarensis
A climber shown here
as a leafy shoot with
inflorescences and a tendril.

Female flower

Male flower

Iodes fruit

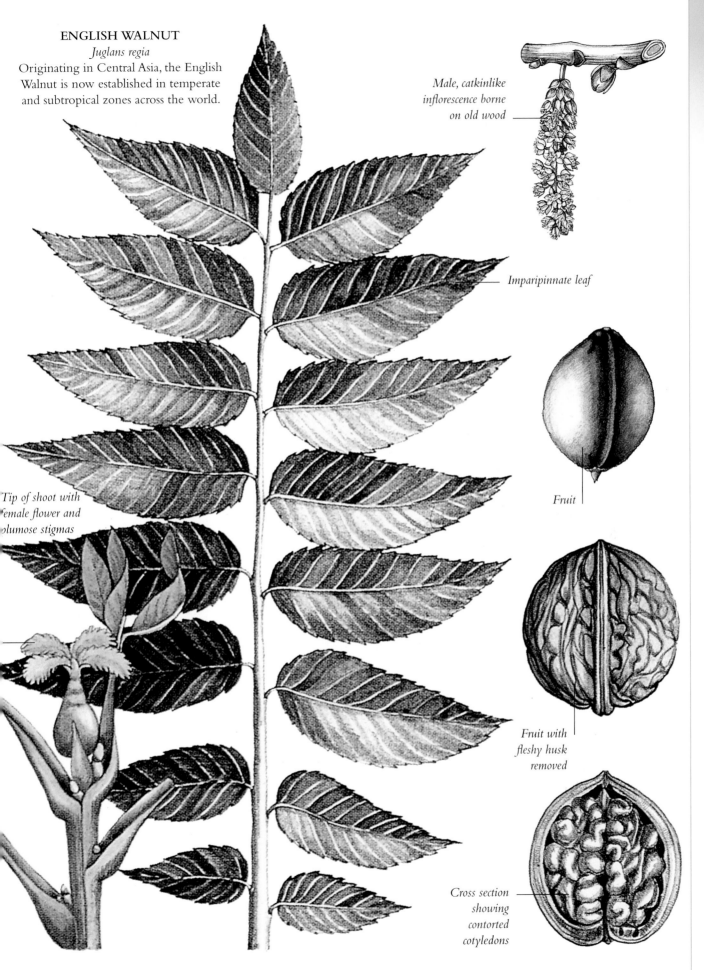

ENGLISH WALNUT
Juglans regia
Originating in Central Asia, the English
Walnut is now established in temperate
and subtropical zones across the world.

*Male, catkinlike
inflorescence borne
on old wood*

Imparipinnate leaf

*Tip of shoot with
female flower and
plumose stigmas*

Fruit

*Fruit with
fleshy husk
removed*

*Cross section
showing
contorted
cotyledons*

MINTS

This large family (Lamiaceae) of herbs, shrubs, and trees grows in all but the polar regions and includes well-known aromatic herbs such as sage, marjoram, oregano, thyme, lavender, rosemary and, of course, mint. This diverse group also features decorative garden plants such as Scarlet Sage *(Salvia splendens)*, making the family hugely important economically. Its commercial significance is further enhanced by the fact that the family, surprisingly, also includes several tropical lumber trees, notably the teaks.

DWARF INDIAN SKULLCAP
Scutellaria indica
The plant here shows opposite leaves and inflorescences with two-lipped corollae.

Detail of shrubby germander flower

SHRUBBY GERMANDER
Teucrium fruticans
This evergreen mint is native to the Mediterranean region.

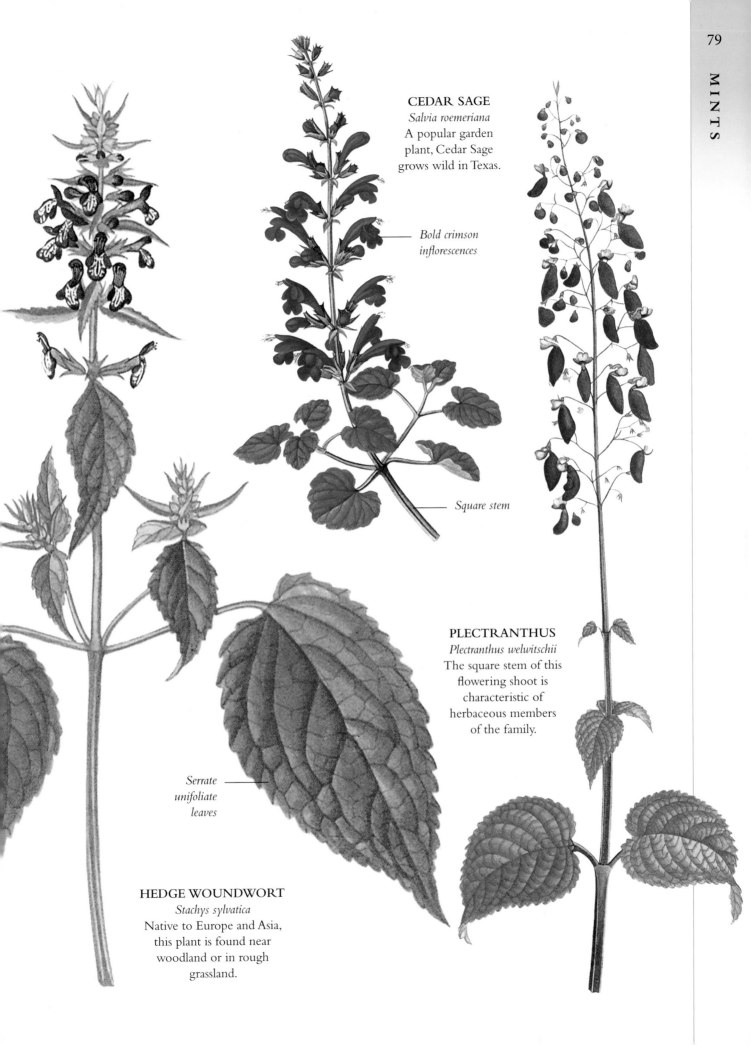

CEDAR SAGE
Salvia roemeriana
A popular garden
plant, Cedar Sage
grows wild in Texas.

*Bold crimson
inflorescences*

Square stem

PLECTRANTHUS
Plectranthus welwitschii
The square stem of this
flowering shoot is
characteristic of
herbaceous members
of the family.

*Serrate
unifoliate
leaves*

HEDGE WOUNDWORT
Stachys sylvatica
Native to Europe and Asia,
this plant is found near
woodland or in rough
grassland.

PEAS AND BEANS

There are almost 20,000 species of peas and beans in the Fabaceae family, making it the third-largest family of flowering plants. As a group, it is second only to cereals in its economic importance. As well as providing a vital source of food, these plants enrich nutrient-poor soil through nitrogen-fixing symbioses with *Rhizobium* bacteria.

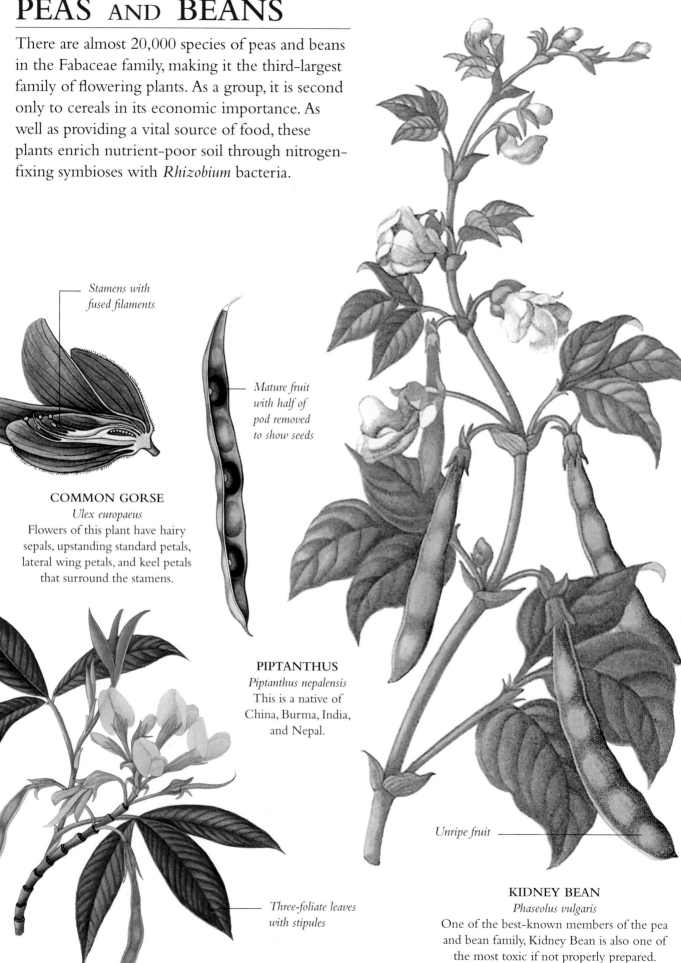

Stamens with fused filaments

COMMON GORSE
Ulex europaeus
Flowers of this plant have hairy sepals, upstanding standard petals, lateral wing petals, and keel petals that surround the stamens.

Mature fruit with half of pod removed to show seeds

PIPTANTHUS
Piptanthus nepalensis
This is a native of China, Burma, India, and Nepal.

Three-foliate leaves with stipules

Unripe fruit

KIDNEY BEAN
Phaseolus vulgaris
One of the best-known members of the pea and bean family, Kidney Bean is also one of the most toxic if not properly prepared.

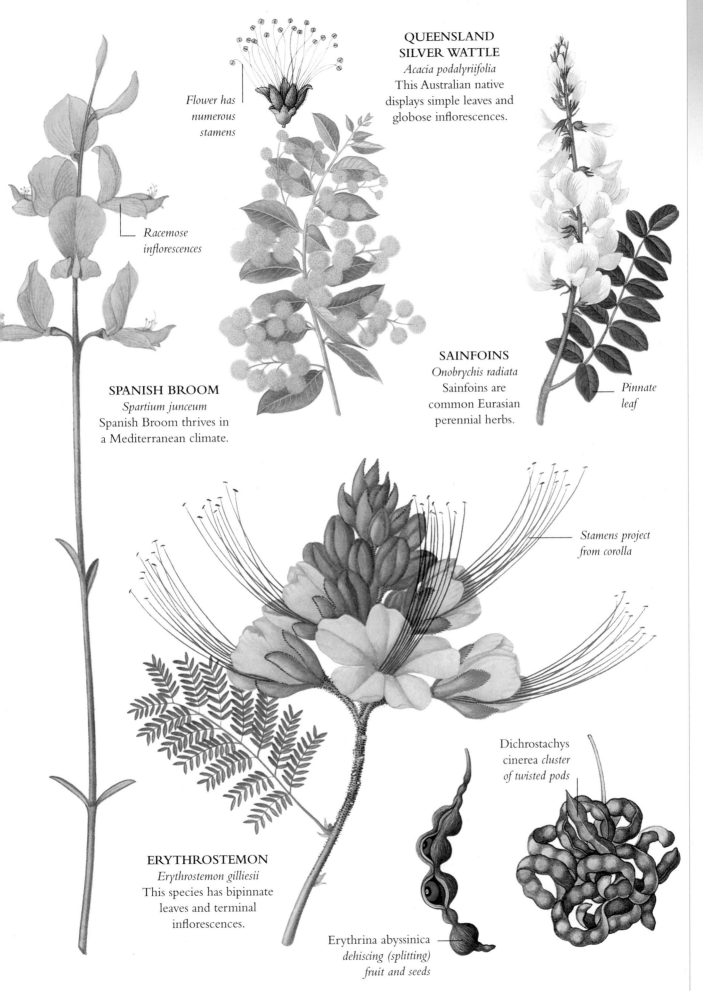

Flower has numerous stamens

QUEENSLAND SILVER WATTLE
Acacia podalyriifolia
This Australian native displays simple leaves and globose inflorescences.

Racemose inflorescences

SAINFOINS
Onobrychis radiata
Sainfoins are common Eurasian perennial herbs.

Pinnate leaf

SPANISH BROOM
Spartium junceum
Spanish Broom thrives in a Mediterranean climate.

Stamens project from corolla

Dichrostachys cinerea *cluster of twisted pods*

ERYTHROSTEMON
Erythrostemon gilliesii
This species has bipinnate leaves and terminal inflorescences.

Erythrina abyssinica *dehiscing (splitting) fruit and seeds*

STRYCHNOS, FLAXES, AND LOOSESTRIFES

The flax family (Linaceae) comprises mainly woody herbs, with over 160 species distributed worldwide. Flax has long been grown for its stem fibers (used in making fabrics and paper) and its oil. The Loganiaceae is a diverse range of plants, found in tropical climates and noted for the poisonous alkaloids produced by several genera (strychnine). Loosestrifes (Lythraceae) are primarily found in the tropics, and many have cosmetic (henna) or ornamental applications.

Spigelia marilandica
fleshy fruit

Flowers have valvate estivation

Long stigma but medium and short stamens

PURPLE LOOSESTRIFE
Lythrum salicaria
Produces three types of flowers (one per individual). The seed-set is higher when the stigma receives pollen from stamens of the same length than when it is pollinated from longer or shorter stamens (pollen transfer shown by arrows).

Long and short stamens and medium stigma

Short stigma, long and medium stamens

STRYCHNOS
Strychnos tieute
Produces highly poisonous alkaloids (strychine, brucine)

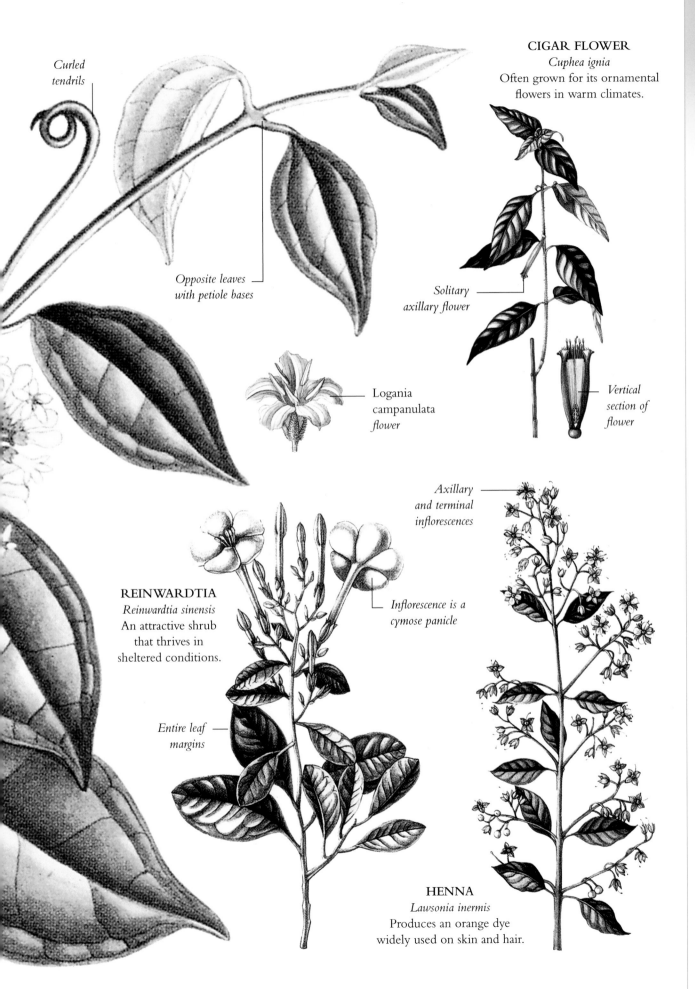

Curled tendrils

CIGAR FLOWER
Cuphea ignia
Often grown for its ornamental flowers in warm climates.

Opposite leaves with petiole bases

Solitary axillary flower

Logania campanulata flower

Vertical section of flower

Axillary and terminal inflorescences

REINWARDTIA
Reinwardtia sinensis
An attractive shrub that thrives in sheltered conditions.

Inflorescence is a cymose panicle

Entire leaf margins

HENNA
Lawsonia inermis
Produces an orange dye widely used on skin and hair.

MAGNOLIAS
AND TULIP TREE

The magnolias (Magnoliaceae) can be either deciduous or evergreen flowering shrubs and trees. Most species are native to tropical and temperate Southeast and East Asia. Fossil records show that the family's evolutionary history stretches back 100 million years or more. The wood of the Tulip Tree is native to eastern North America, where it provides a valuable commercial lumber product.

STAR MAGNOLIA
Magnolia stellata
The Japanese Star Magnolia shows a leaf and shoot bearing bracts on the flower stalks.

Sphedamnocarpus flower with filament bases united in a ring

SPHEDAMNOCARPUS
Sphedamnocarpus pruriens
The yellow flowers of this plant have five sepals and five petals.

Dehisced fruits of Magnolia grandiflora

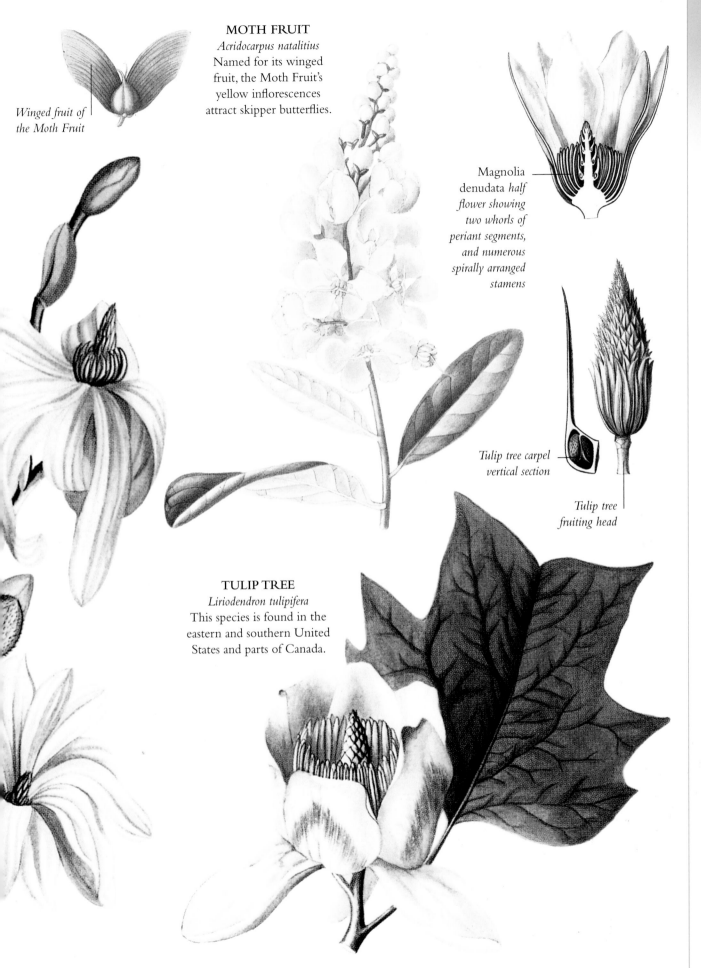

Winged fruit of the Moth Fruit

MOTH FRUIT
Acridocarpus natalitius
Named for its winged fruit, the Moth Fruit's yellow inflorescences attract skipper butterflies.

Magnolia *denudata half flower showing two whorls of periant segments, and numerous spirally arranged stamens*

Tulip tree carpel vertical section

Tulip tree fruiting head

TULIP TREE
Liriodendron tulipifera
This species is found in the eastern and southern United States and parts of Canada.

MALLOWS AND MARCGRAVIAS

The Malvaceae family of mallows, hollyhocks, and cotton has representatives worldwide, although most species are either tropical or subtropical. Cotton is the most economically important species, but the family also produces edible fruits such as okra, or ladies' fingers. The Marcgraviaceae family of tropical climbers, shrubs, and trees is notable for a number of interesting features such as highly modified nectaries and deciduous flower caps.

Deciduous flower cap

Nectar cup

MARCGRAVIA
Marcgravia umbellata
The flower petals of this climbing plant from the American tropics form a cap that falls off when the flower opens.

Numerous roots growing from stem

MARCGRAVIA
Marcgravia exauriculata
Shown here is the tip of a shoot with adult leaves and inflorescences.

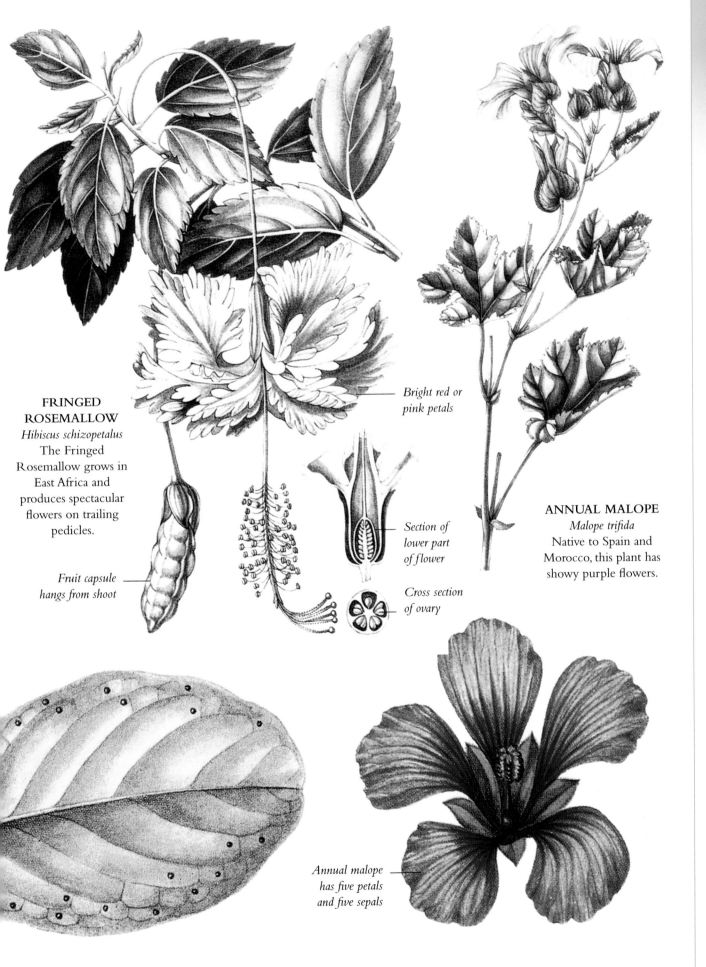

FRINGED ROSEMALLOW
Hibiscus schizopetalus
The Fringed Rosemallow grows in East Africa and produces spectacular flowers on trailing pedicles.

Fruit capsule hangs from shoot

Bright red or pink petals

Section of lower part of flower

Cross section of ovary

ANNUAL MALOPE
Malope trifida
Native to Spain and Morocco, this plant has showy purple flowers.

Annual malope has five petals and five sepals

BUNCHFLOWERS AND MEDUSANDRAS

Apart from 25 species in Chile, all the trees and shrubs in the bunchflower family (Melianthaceae) grow in South Africa. Their soft wood is often used for making carvings, and these plants also have medicinal properties. There are two species of medusandras (Medusandraceae), both endemic to Cameroon. Both species are trees that exhibit simple, pinnately veined leaves with long petioles, and flowers borne in pendulous, catkinlike inflorescences.

Inflorescence with flowers and immature fruits

Capsule

Half flower with irregular petals

Leaves are pinnate

HONEY BUSH
Melianthus pectinatus
South Africa has the largest variety of
Melianthus bunchflowers, with six species
living in both wet and dry habitats.

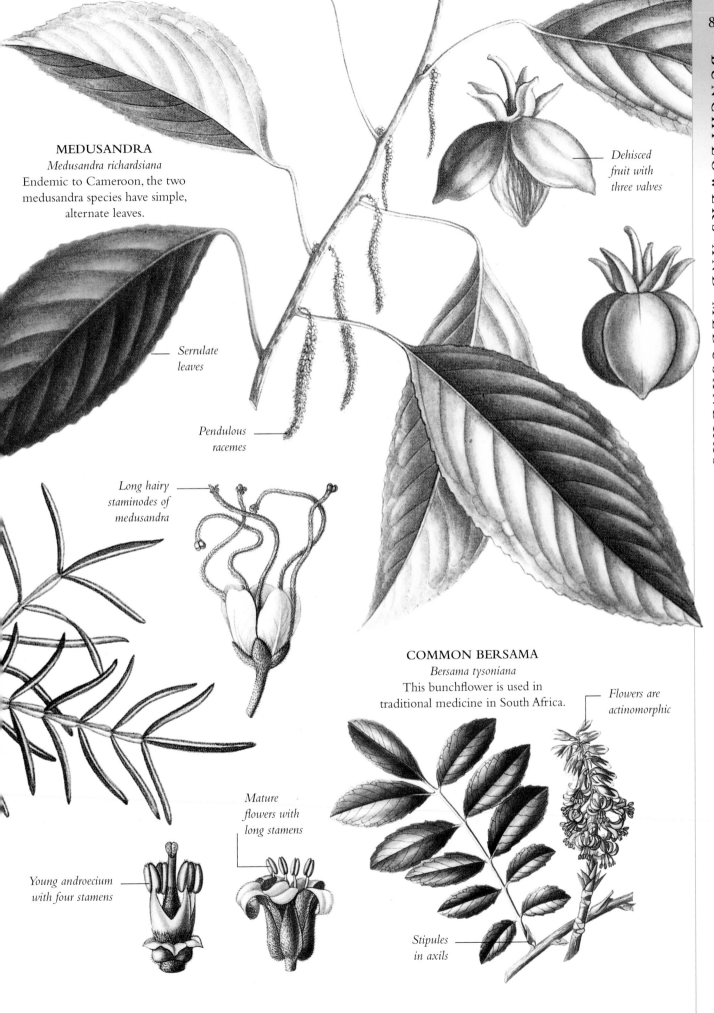

MEDUSANDRA
Medusandra richardsiana
Endemic to Cameroon, the two
medusandra species have simple,
alternate leaves.

Dehisced
fruit with
three valves

Serrulate
leaves

Pendulous
racemes

Long hairy
staminodes of
medusandra

COMMON BERSAMA
Bersama tysoniana
This bunchflower is used in
traditional medicine in South Africa.

Flowers are
actinomorphic

Mature
flowers with
long stamens

Young androecium
with four stamens

Stipules
in axils

ICE PLANTS AND LIVING STONES

Ice plants are succulent annual or perennial herbs or small shrubs, usually with daisylike flowers, forming brilliant sheets of color when growing en masse. They are named for the tiny, glistening, nipplelike structures that cover the plants, giving them a frosty appearance despite the fact that most species live in warm-temperate, subtropical, or even hot desert regions. Living stones are part of the same family (Mesembryanthemaceae). Their compact, succulent leaves take on a striking resemblance to the rock formations on which they live.

FAUCARIA
Faucaria tigrina
Faucaria displays a dense
rosette of spiny leaves.

*Redflush half
flower with
numerous
stamens*

REDFLUSH
Lampranthus species
The plant's shoot has
succulent leaves and
terminal, solitary flowers.

RUSCHIA UNCINATA
Native to South Africa and
Namibia, a flowering shoot
of this ice plant is shown.

**LITHOPS
PSEUDOTRUNCATELLA**
Living stones' two succulent leaves
give them a pebblelike appearance.

LITHOPS LESLIEI
Flowers arise from the
fissure in this living
stone plant.

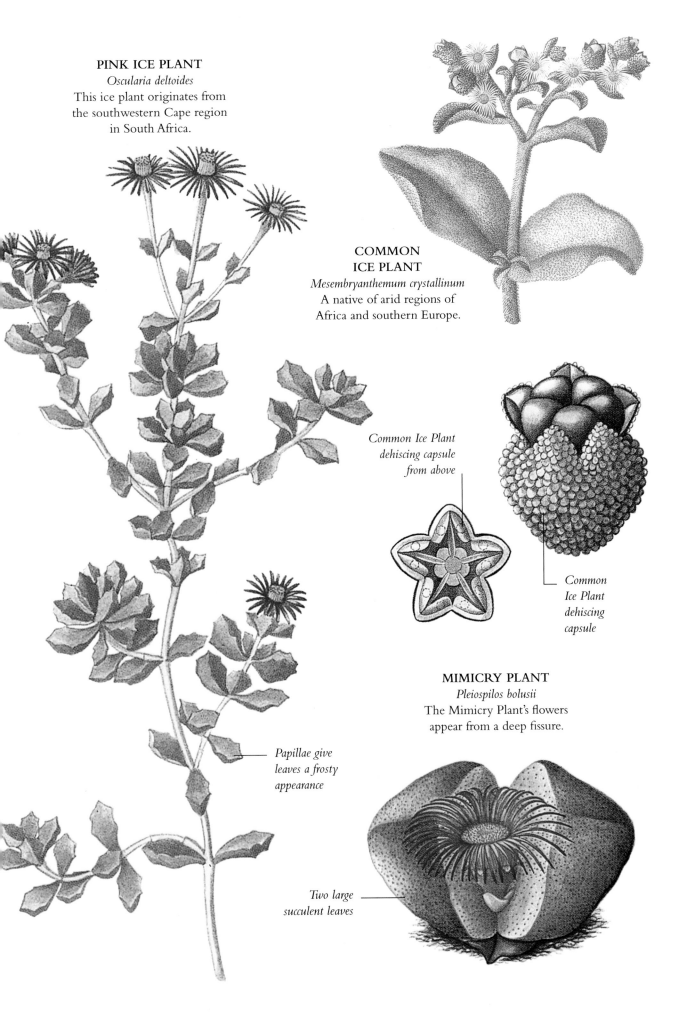

PINK ICE PLANT
Oscularia deltoides
This ice plant originates from
the southwestern Cape region
in South Africa.

**COMMON
ICE PLANT**
Mesembryanthemum crystallinum
A native of arid regions of
Africa and southern Europe.

*Common Ice Plant
dehiscing capsule
from above*

*Common
Ice Plant
dehiscing
capsule*

MIMICRY PLANT
Pleiospilos bolusii
The Mimicry Plant's flowers
appear from a deep fissure.

*Papillae give
leaves a frosty
appearance*

*Two large
succulent leaves*

MONIMIACEAE AND MYOPORACEAE

The small trees and shrubs in the family Monimiaceae grow in the tropics and subtropics of South America, South Africa, and eastern Australasia. Species include *Monimia rotundifolia* and *Tambourissa elliptica*. Wood from these plants is used locally for construction, and aromatic oils extracted from the bark and leaves are used in medicine and perfumery. Plants in the family Myoporaceae live most extensively in Australia, where they are widely grown as ornamentals. Examples include Emu Bush, Fuchsia Bush, and Sticky Boobialla.

Solitary flowers in leaf axils

Monimia rotundifolia *axillary inflorescence*

Opposite, simple, entire leaves

Tambourissa elliptica *vertical section of fruit*

FUCHSIA BUSH
Eremophila glabra
The fruit of this species is an important food for birds.

*Flower contains
two-lipped corolla*

EMU BUSH
Eremophila bignoniiflora
This plant is grown
extensively as an
ornamental in Australia.

*Stamen has
divergent
anthers*

*Alternate
enciform
leaves*

**STICKY
BOOBIALLA**
Myoporum petiolatum
Cultivated in Australia
as ornamentals,
windbreaks, and hedges.

*Linear
leaves*

PIGEONWOOD
Hedycarya arborea
This species bears
axillary inflorescences
and distinctive leaves.

*Sticky Boobialla
flower with
fused calyx*

*Opened corolla
with stamens*

NUTMEG AND MYRSINES

Nutmeg is a member of the Myristicaceae family of trees (usually evergreen) that grow mostly in tropical lowland rain forests. The wood from these trees makes poor-quality lumber and exudes a reddish sap when wounded. The Nutmeg tree also provides the spices nutmeg (from the seed) and mace (from the aril). There are more than 1,320 species of myrsines (Myrsinaceae), which are trees and shrubs with leathery, evergreen leaves growing in the Southern Hemisphere.

Virola
glaziovii
inflorescence

Leaves alternate
and entire

Female flower
opened up

Sterile stamens
(staminodes)

Single-seeded
fleshy fruit

Alternate,
entire leaves

AFRICAN BOXWOOD
Myrsine africana
Bears unusually small leaves for the
family, and metallic-purple fruits.

NUTMEG
Myristica fragrans
Originating in the
Moluccas, Nutmeg trees are
now widely cultivated.

Nutmeg fruit
split showing
aril and seed

Knema
pectinata
entire leaf

Fruit
(nutmeg)
split open

Shoot with
male flowers

Seed covered
with red aril

Axillary
inflorescences

ARDISIA
Ardisia humilis
Often grown in
greenhouses or as a house
plant, this myrsine has
bright red fruit.

Half flower
bud

Resin ducts

EUCALYPTS AND TROPICAL PITCHER PLANTS

Eucalypts (Myrtaceae) grow as trees or shrubs across South America, sub-Saharan Africa, Southeast Asia, and Australia. They are cultivated for lumber and oils for the perfume industry. Three species of tropical pitcher plants (Nepenthaceae) grow in northern Australia, but their biggest diversity is in Indonesia and the Philippines. These carnivorous plants vary in size, although some have pitchers big enough to hold up to half a gallon (2 liters) of water. Animals entering the pitcher cannot climb the slippery sides and eventually drown in the liquid.

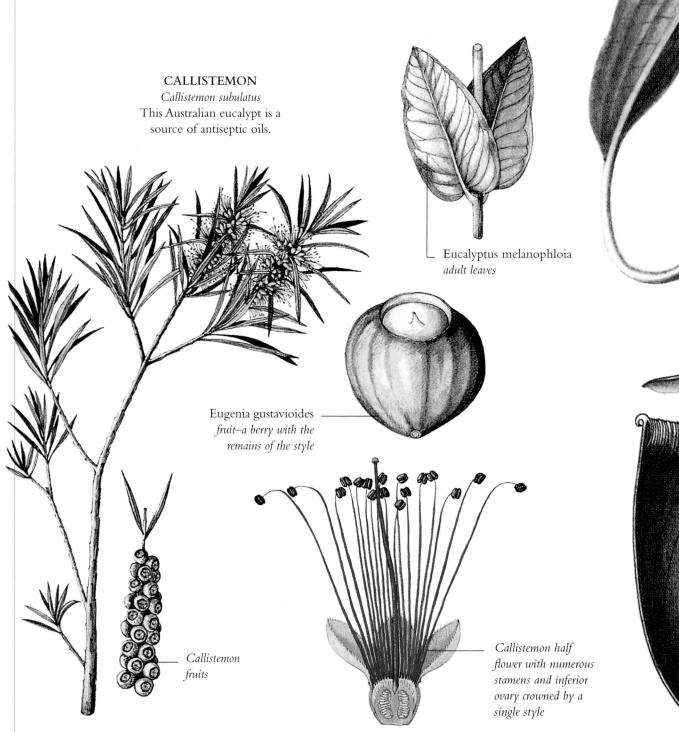

Leaf

CALLISTEMON
Callistemon subulatus
This Australian eucalypt is a source of antiseptic oils.

Eucalyptus melanophloia
adult leaves

Eugenia gustavioides
fruit—a berry with the remains of the style

Callistemon fruits

Callistemon half flower with numerous stamens and inferior ovary crowned by a single style

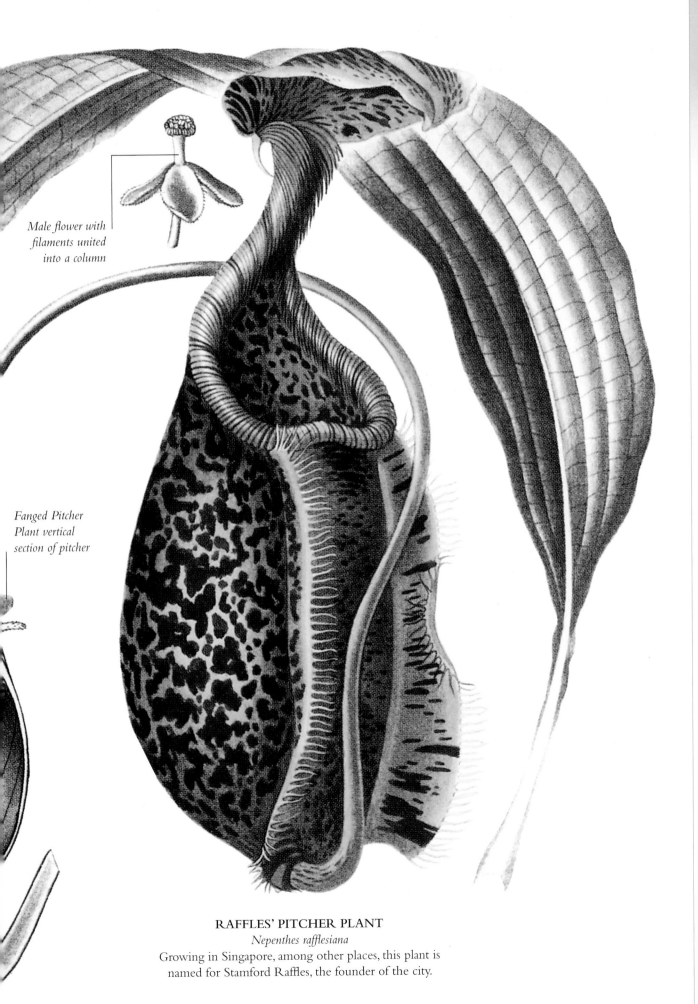

*Male flower with
filaments united
into a column*

*Fanged Pitcher
Plant vertical
section of pitcher*

RAFFLES' PITCHER PLANT
Nepenthes rafflesiana
Growing in Singapore, among other places, this plant is
named for Stamford Raffles, the founder of the city.

BOUGAINVILLEAS AND WATER LILIES

Bougainvilleas (Nyctaginaceae) are noted, and often cultivated, for the bright, colorful bracts that surround the flowers of many species. Water lilies (Nymphaeaceae) are freshwater aquatic herbs that occur worldwide in habitats where they may be either fully or partially submerged. Many genera have floating leaves, some of which (*Victoria amazonica,* for example) are enormous.

Leaves are always submerged

BARCLAYA
Barclaya motleyi
All four species of *Barclaya* are endemic to tropical Indo-Malaysia.

Marvel of Peru flowers are surrounded by calyxlike bracts

Indehiscent fruit

Bougainvillea spectabilis *flowers surrounded by colored bracts*

MARVEL OF PERU
Mirabilis jalapa
The name of this species relates to its polychromatic flowers, which can be white, yellow, or red.

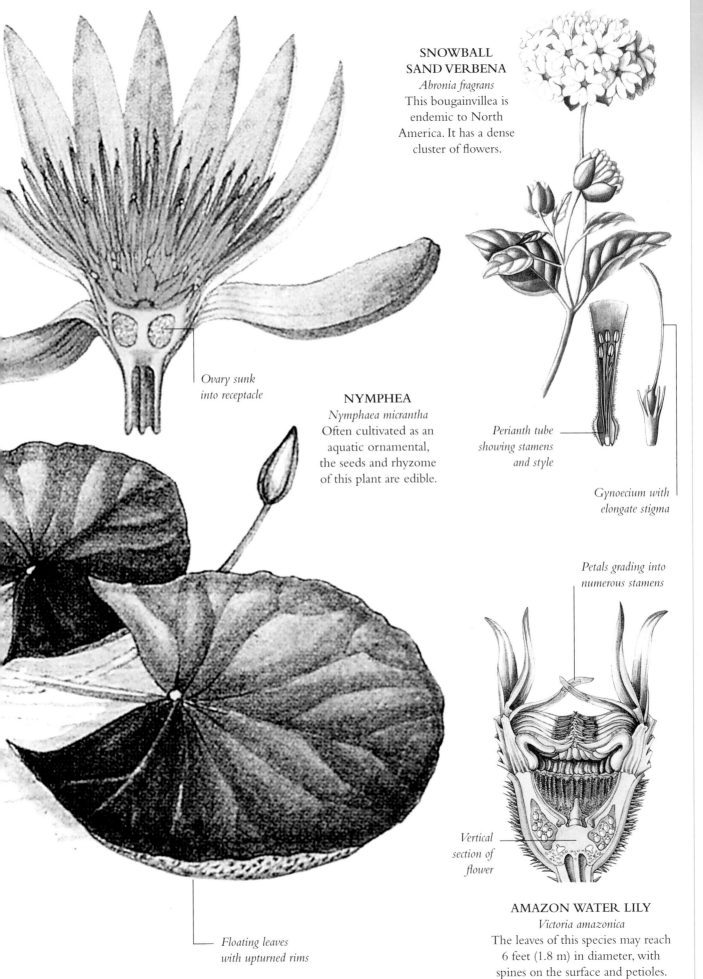

**SNOWBALL
SAND VERBENA**
Abronia fragrans
This bougainvillea is
endemic to North
America. It has a dense
cluster of flowers.

*Ovary sunk
into receptacle*

NYMPHEA
Nymphaea micrantha
Often cultivated as an
aquatic ornamental,
the seeds and rhyzome
of this plant are edible.

*Perianth tube
showing stamens
and style*

*Gynoecium with
elongate stigma*

*Petals grading into
numerous stamens*

*Vertical
section of
flower*

*Floating leaves
with upturned rims*

AMAZON WATER LILY
Victoria amazonica
The leaves of this species may reach
6 feet (1.8 m) in diameter, with
spines on the surface and petioles.

OLIVES, WILD PLANES, AND AFRICAN WALNUTS

The olive family (Oleaceae) includes ash trees and *Forsythia* species as well as olives, which have been cultivated for thousands of years for their edible fruits and oil. Ash is a valuable lumber crop. The families Ochnaceae (wild planes) and Olacaceae (including African walnuts) are largely tropical.

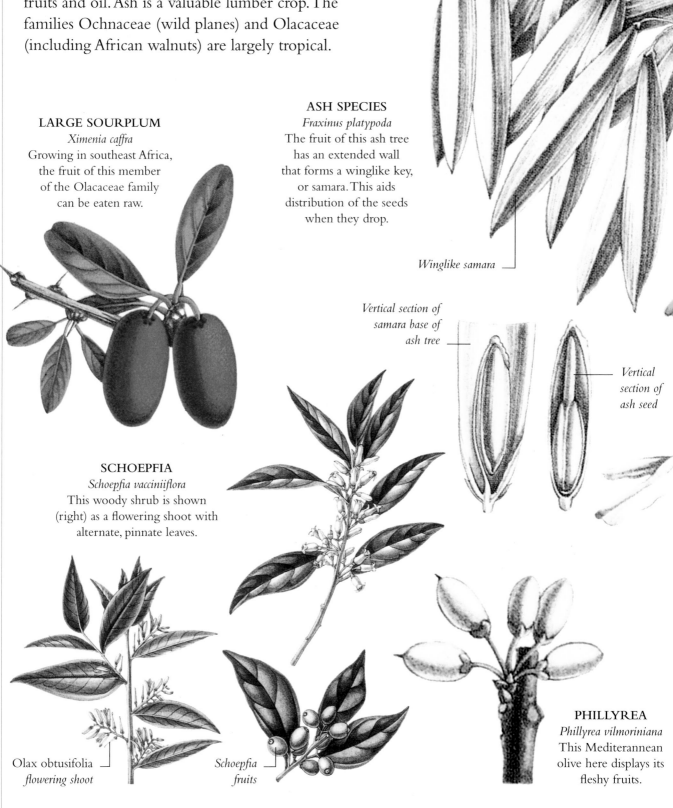

LARGE SOURPLUM
Ximenia caffra
Growing in southeast Africa, the fruit of this member of the Olacaceae family can be eaten raw.

ASH SPECIES
Fraxinus platypoda
The fruit of this ash tree has an extended wall that forms a winglike key, or samara. This aids distribution of the seeds when they drop.

Winglike samara

Vertical section of samara base of ash tree

Vertical section of ash seed

SCHOEPFIA
Schoepfia vacciniiflora
This woody shrub is shown (right) as a flowering shoot with alternate, pinnate leaves.

Olax obtusifolia
flowering shoot

Schoepfia fruits

PHILLYREA
Phillyrea vilmoriniana
This Mediterannean olive here displays its fleshy fruits.

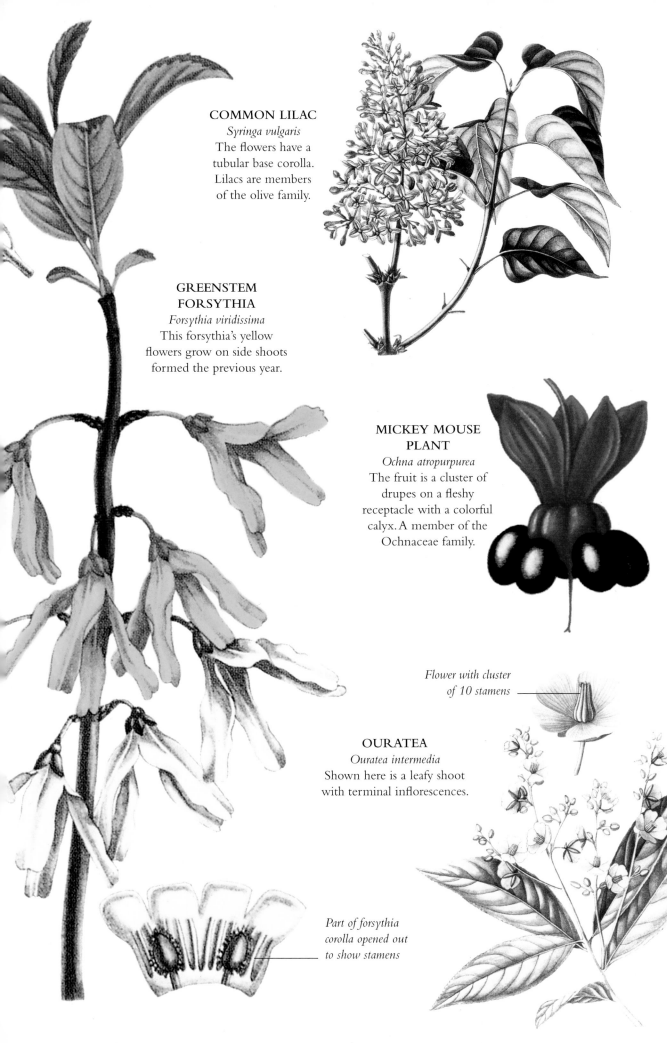

COMMON LILAC
Syringa vulgaris
The flowers have a
tubular base corolla.
Lilacs are members
of the olive family.

**GREENSTEM
FORSYTHIA**
Forsythia viridissima
This forsythia's yellow
flowers grow on side shoots
formed the previous year.

**MICKEY MOUSE
PLANT**
Ochna atropurpurea
The fruit is a cluster of
drupes on a fleshy
receptacle with a colorful
calyx. A member of the
Ochnaceae family.

*Flower with cluster
of 10 stamens*

OURATEA
Ouratea intermedia
Shown here is a leafy shoot
with terminal inflorescences.

*Part of forsythia
corolla opened out
to show stamens*

EVENING PRIMROSES AND WOOD SORRELS

The evening primroses (Onagraceae) are mainly perennial to annual herbs. Fuchsias are widely cultivated as ornamentals. The wood sorrel family (Oxalidaceae) of small trees, shrubs, climbers, and perennial herbs is native to the tropics. Many members have edible leaves, tubers, or fruit.

Splitting fruit of Biophytum sensitivum

SENSITIVE PLANT
Biophytum sensitivum
Native to South and Southeast Asia, the leaves of this annual herb bend when touched.

Pinnate leaves; terminal leaflet reduced to a bristle

Flower with petals removed

Androecium and gynoecium

CHILEAN OXALIS
Oxalis adenophylla
The leaves of this species of wood sorrel fold downward at night and in cold weather.

Lopezia
coronota
flower

CODLINS AND CREAM
Epilobium hirsutum
This member of the evening
primrose family grows in cool
temperate environments on every
continent but Antarctica.

*Ripe fruit
dehiscing,
releasing seeds*

*Partly opened
flower with
petals removed*

*Petals on upper
side of flower*

COMMON
EVENING PRIMROSE
Oenothera biennis
The blooms are yellow,
with four bilobed petals.

FUCHSIA
Fuchsia alpestris
Native to South America,
this plant's free sepals are
longer than the magenta
petals. It is pollinated by
hummingbirds, bees, flies,
and butterflies.

*Half flower
showing long
free sepals*

PEONIES

There are more than 30 species of peonies (Paeoniaceae), perennial rhizomatous herbs or soft-wooded shrubs with large, showy flowers. The flowers are white, pink, red, purple, or yellow; they are solitary and mostly terminal. The dried roots of certain species have been used as a sedative in Chinese herbal medicines for as long as 2,500 years.

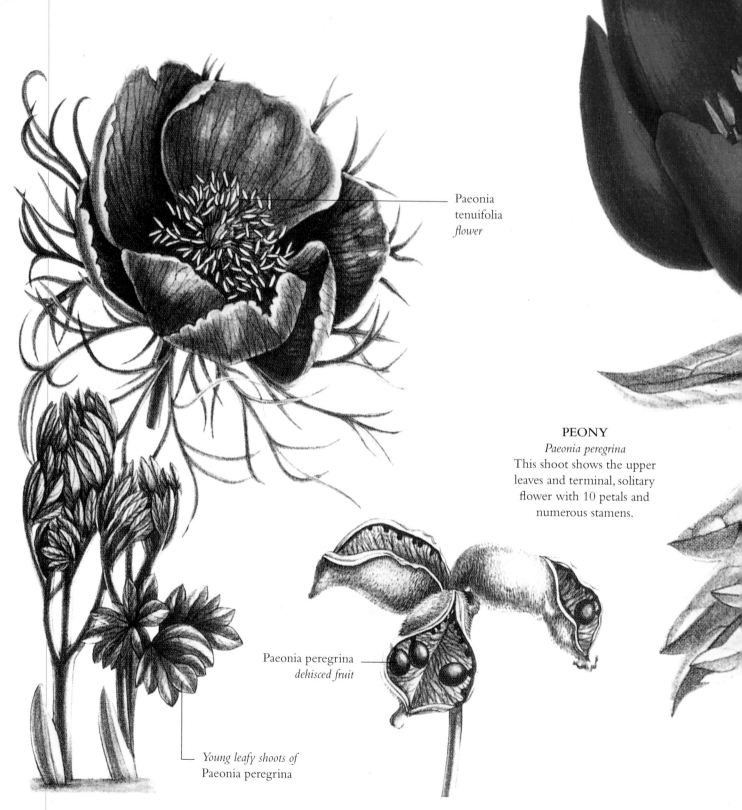

Paeonia
tenuifolia
flower

PEONY
Paeonia peregrina
This shoot shows the upper leaves and terminal, solitary flower with 10 petals and numerous stamens.

Paeonia peregrina
dehisced fruit

Young leafy shoots of
Paeonia peregrina

Young fruit of Peonia
wittmanniana

Peonia mascula
*fruit with five
follicles*

Paeonia peregrina *young
fruit comprising three follicles*

POPPIES AND FUMITORIES

These mainly herbaceous annuals or perennials (family Papaveraceae) grow mostly in the Northern Hemisphere, in open meadows, on rocky mountain slopes, or in disturbed ground. The stems, leaves, and other parts of many species contain a well-developed system of secretory canals that produce yellow, milky, or watery latex. In some species this secretion is the source of opium.

Half flower showing spurred petal and elongated ovary

ROCK FUMEWORT
Corydalis lutea
Shown here with much divided leaves and irregular flowers in a racemose inflorescence.

Delicate white inflorescences

PTERIDOPHYLLUM RACEMOSUM
A native of Japan, *Pteridophyllum* is shown here displaying its fernlike leaves.

PLUME POPPY
Macleaya cordata
A plant native to China and Japan.

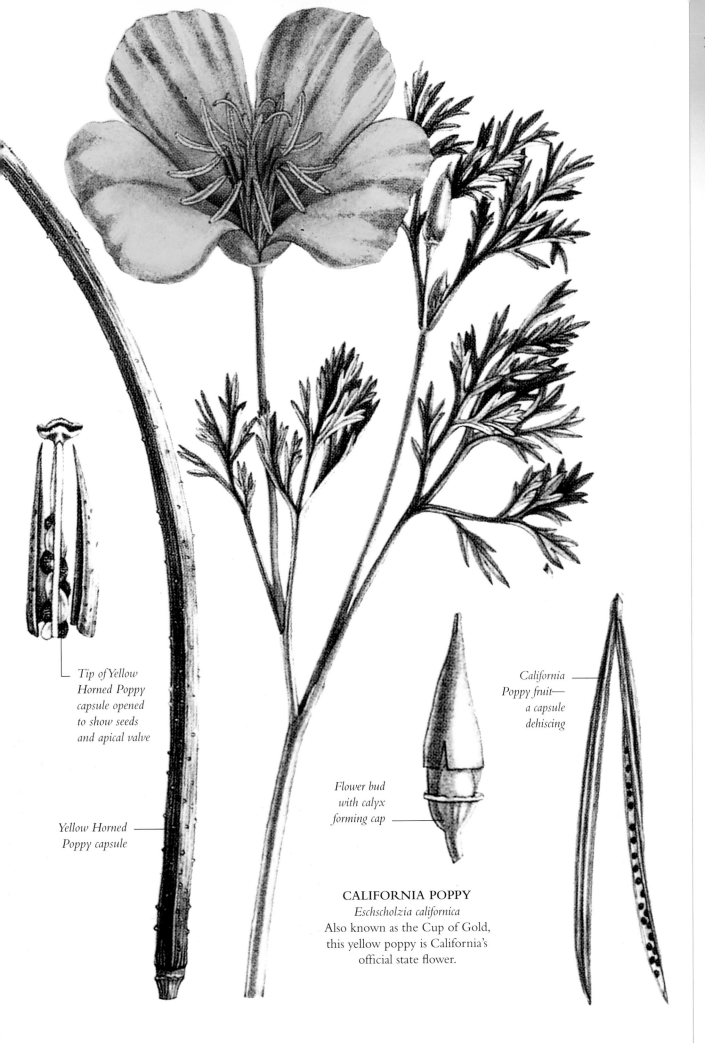

Tip of Yellow Horned Poppy capsule opened to show seeds and apical valve

Yellow Horned Poppy capsule

Flower bud with calyx forming cap

California Poppy fruit— a capsule dehiscing

CALIFORNIA POPPY
Eschscholzia californica
Also known as the Cup of Gold, this yellow poppy is California's official state flower.

PASSION FLOWERS AND PEPPERS

Passion flowers (Passifloraceae) grow throughout the tropics but are also successfully cultivated as garden ornamentals in temperate regions. Their fruit is edible and is used commercially in juices but their leaves are generally poisonous. Tropical trees, shrubs, lianas, and herbs of the pepper family (Piperaceae) are found across Central and South America, and in Africa, Asia, and Australia. *Piper nigrum* is the source of commercial peppercorns.

SILVER HEART
Peperomia marmorata
This pepper is native to Brazil and is seen here displaying its flower spikes and leaves with the light, often silvery veins for which it is named.

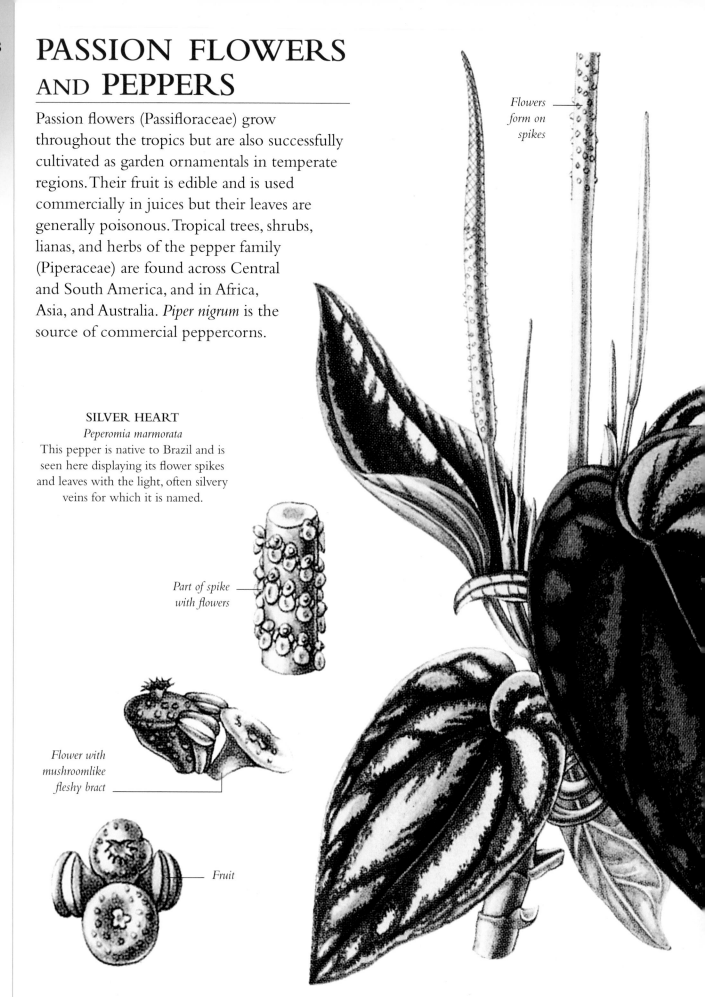

Flowers form on spikes

Part of spike with flowers

Flower with mushroomlike fleshy bract

Fruit

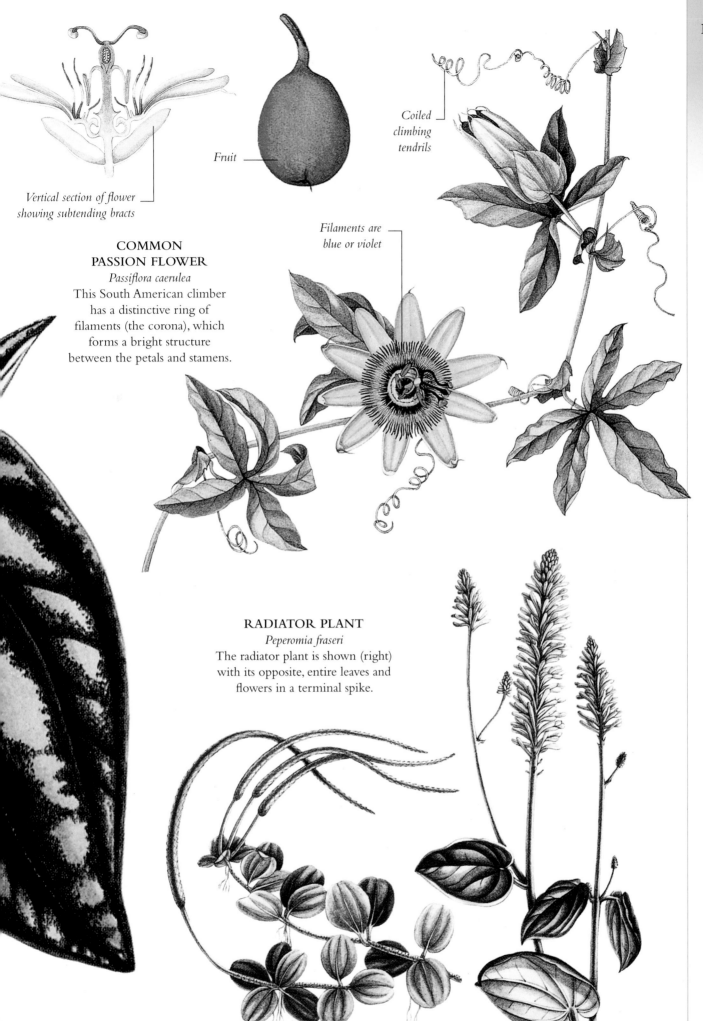

Vertical section of flower showing subtending bracts

Fruit

Coiled climbing tendrils

Filaments are blue or violet

COMMON PASSION FLOWER
Passiflora caerulea
This South American climber has a distinctive ring of filaments (the corona), which forms a bright structure between the petals and stamens.

RADIATOR PLANT
Peperomia fraseri
The radiator plant is shown (right) with its opposite, entire leaves and flowers in a terminal spike.

PARCHMENT BARKS, SEA LAVENDERS, AND THRIFTS

The parchment bark shrubs (Pittosporaceae), including *Marianthus* and cheesewood species, originate from sub-Saharan Africa and Australasia but are widely cultivated as ornamentals elsewhere.

The sea lavender and thrift family (Plumbaginaceae) grow on all continents apart from Antarctica. They are shrubs, herbs, or lianas with spirally arranged leaves.

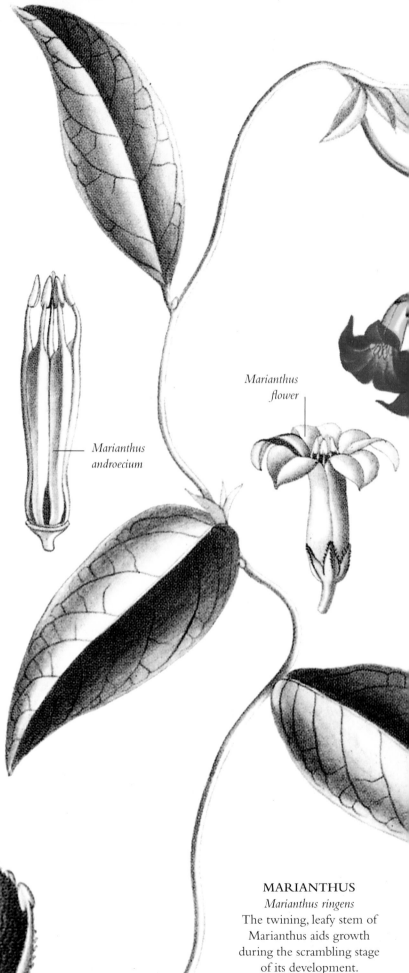

Marianthus androecium

Marianthus flower

STIFFLEAF CHEESEWOOD
Pittosporum crassifolium
This plant can have purple, white, or greenish flowers.

Cheesewood gynoecium from female flower with vestigial stamens

MARIANTHUS
Marianthus ringens
The twining, leafy stem of Marianthus aids growth during the scrambling stage of its development.

*Evergreen,
leathery leaves*

*Five petals are
characteristic of
this species*

*Flowers in
branched
panicles*

SEA LAVENDER
Limonium imbricatum
Endemic to Tenerife, the plant is
shown here displaying part of the
tap root and its rosette of leaves.

CAPE LEADWORT
Plumbago auriculata
Its simple leaves and pale
blue flowers make this a
beautiful climbing plant.

RIVERWEEDS AND PHLOX

Riverweeds (Podostemaceae) are seasonal aquatics that can resemble liverworts, mosses, or algae. They grow on rocks in torrential waters in the tropics and warm-temperate regions. The phlox family (Polemoniaceae) is predominantly a temperate New World group, though the genus *Polemonium* is widespread in northern temperate regions.

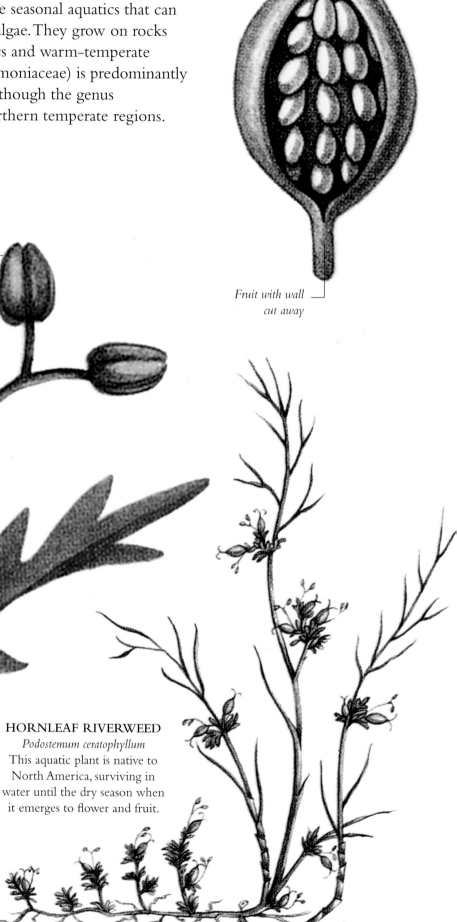

Fruit with wall cut away

Flower with two divided bracts

HORNLEAF RIVERWEED
Podostemum ceratophyllum
This aquatic plant is native to North America, surviving in water until the dry season when it emerges to flower and fruit.

Lilac colored inflorescences

CALIFORNIA GILIA
Gilia achilleifolia
This herb grows wild mainly in arid western North America, although it can be found as far south as Chile or Argentina.

Gilia flower opened out to show insertion of stamens between corolla lobes

Flowers usually pink or lavender

FALSE BABYSTARS
Linanthus androsaceus
Native to California, this colorful plant grows pink or lavender flowers with yellow or white throats.

Phlox paniculata opened to show irregular insertion of stamens

LOESELIA
Loeselia cordifolia
Seen here is a Loeselia shoot with toothed, opposite leaves and small cymose clusters of flowers.

MILKWORTS AND PURSLANES

The herbs, shrubs, small trees, climbers, and even saprophytes of the milkwort family (Polygalaceae) can often look similar to pea and bean species. Unlike the latter, they have no great economic importance. Purslanes and *Lewisia* species (Portulacaceae) are adapted for survival in more arid areas.

Flower with lateral sepals removed

XANTHOPHYLLUM
Xanthophyllum scortechinii
Xanthophyllum is most at home in lowland tropical rain forests in Southeast Asia and northern Australia.

Irregular flowers

POLYGALA
Polygala apopetala
Milkworts such as this are found throughout most of the world apart from New Zealand, some southern Pacific islands, and the very highest latitudes.

Xanthophyllum fruit

Winged fruits, or samaras, of the African Violet Tree, a milkwort

**MOSS-ROSE
PURSLANE**
Portulaca grandiflora
The overlapping petals
can be seen on this
half flower.

*Mature Miner's Lettuce
capsule with one of two
persistent sepals removed*

*Petals may be pink,
orange, yellow, or
almost white*

*Flower stalks
are erect before
pollination,
curved down
afterward and
erect when
bearing fruit*

SISKIYOU LEWISIA
Lewisia cotyledon
A native of Oregon and
northern California, where
it grows in rocky,
mountainous terrain.

*Basal rosette
of leaves*

MINER'S LETTUCE
Claytonia perfoliata
So called because it was
eaten by miners during
the California gold rush
in the 19th century.

PRIMULAS

Primulas (Primulaceae) are herbs with often showy tubular flowers and stamens opposite the corolla lobes. The primula family has 21 genera and around 900 species, many of which are cultivated as decorative ornamentals.

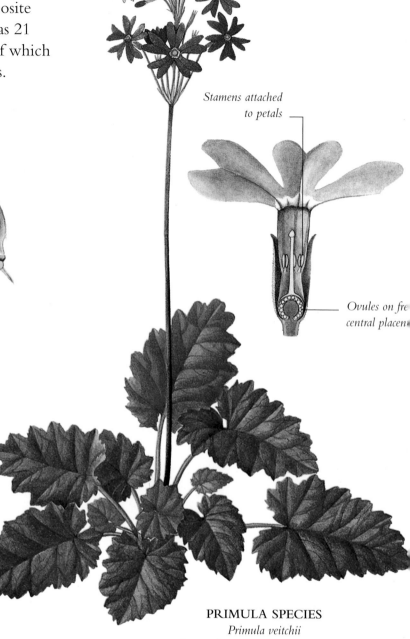

Stamens attached to petals

Ovules on fre central placen

Petals curved backward

PRIDE OF OHIO
Dodecatheon meadia
Bears a basal rosette of leaves with flowers on leafless stalks.

PRIMULA SPECIES
Primula veitchii
A mat-forming plant with a basal rosette, this species is widely cultivated.

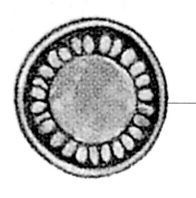

Cross section of Primula veitchii ovary

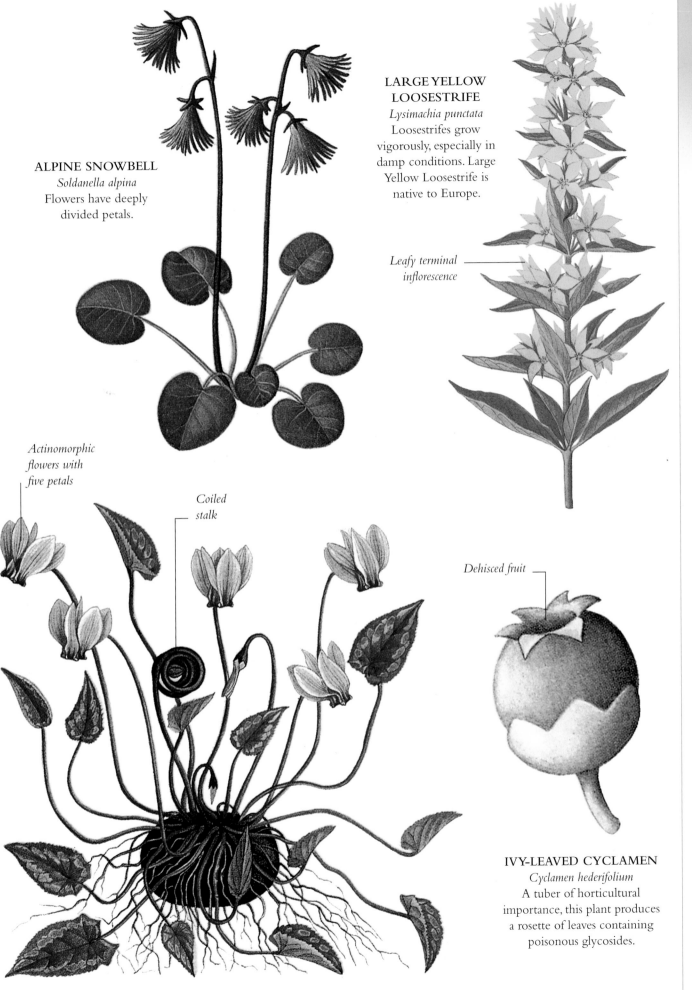

ALPINE SNOWBELL
Soldanella alpina
Flowers have deeply
divided petals.

**LARGE YELLOW
LOOSESTRIFE**
Lysimachia punctata
Loosestrifes grow
vigorously, especially in
damp conditions. Large
Yellow Loosestrife is
native to Europe.

*Leafy terminal
inflorescence*

*Actinomorphic
flowers with
five petals*

*Coiled
stalk*

Dehisced fruit

IVY-LEAVED CYCLAMEN
Cyclamen hederifolium
A tuber of horticultural
importance, this plant produces
a rosette of leaves containing
poisonous glycosides.

PROTEAS AND RAFFLESIAS

Proteas (Proteaceae) are perennial trees and shrubs, native to the Southern Hemisphere and growing in a range of habitats from lowland grassland to rain forests and alpine meadows. Rafflesias (Rafflesiaceae) are stem and root parasites from Southeast Asia and China. They have no stems. *Rafflesia arnoldii is* claimed to have the largest flower in the world, some examples growing to more than 39 inches (1 meter) across.

Projecting style from each Silkoak flower

Pollen presenter

SILKOAK
Grevillea robusta
A native of Australia, the Silkoak (above) has deeply divided leaves and thrives in subtropical or dry rainforest environments.

TREE PINCUSHION
Leucospermum conocarpodendron
This leafy shoot has a terminal conelike inflorescence, each flower with a conspicuous arrow-shaped pollen presenter.

Flower with stamens fused to perianth segments

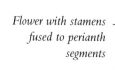

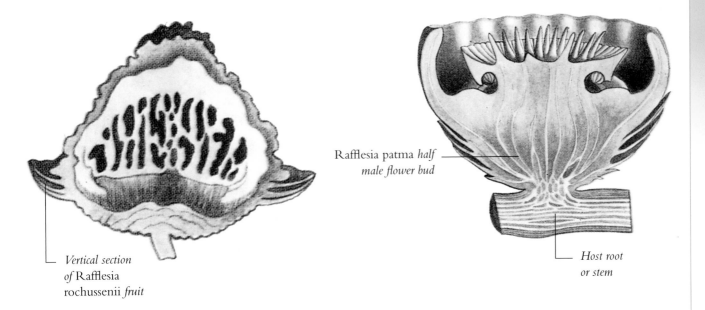

Vertical section of Rafflesia rochussenii *fruit*

Rafflesia patma *half male flower bud*

Host root or stem

CORPSE FLOWER

Rafflesia manillana
Growing in the Philippines, this *Rafflesia* is named for the malodorous stench of rotting flesh that it exudes.

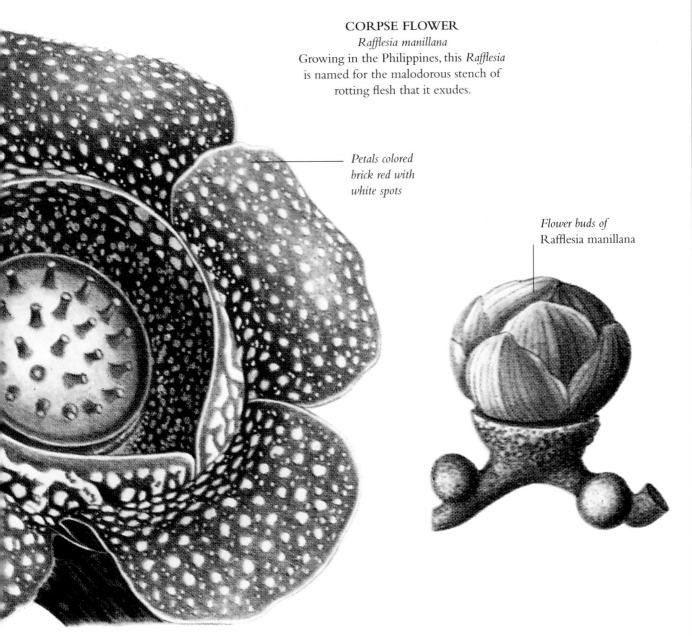

Petals colored brick red with white spots

Flower buds of Rafflesia manillana

BUTTERCUPS

Buttercups (Ranunculaceae) are perennial or sometimes annual herbs or lianas that grow on every continent except Antarctica. Most species prefer wet or moist conditions and a few are aquatic. Gardeners prize several types as showy herbaceous border plants although some are highly poisonous. Victorian medical books give lurid details of the symptoms and deaths of gardeners who have inadvertently eaten *Aconitum* tubers, having confused them with Jerusalem artichokes.

TINY MOUSETAIL
Myosurus minimus
This annual plant grows
on riverbanks or moist meadowland
in Europe, Asia, North Africa, and
North America.

GLOBE FLOWER
Trollius europaeus
Native to Europe and western
Asia, Globe Flowers grow in
damp ground and shade.

LESSER MEADOW-RUE
Thalictrum minus
Shoots showing leaves
and flowers in a terminal
inflorescence.

Fig-shaped
leaves

FIG BUTTERCUP
Ficaria verna
Entire plant, showing
tuberous roots.

COLORADO BLUE COLUMBINE
Aquilegia caerulea
A leafy shoot displaying regular flowers with spurred perianth segments.

ALPINE CLEMATIS
Clematis alpina
This shoot shows axillary flowers and opposite leaves with long petioles to aid climbing.

WINTER ACONITE
Eranthis hyemalis
Found in southern Europe and much of Asia.

LILIES-OF-THE-FIELD
Anemone coronaria
A Mediterranean native also known as Poppy Anemone and Spanish Marigold.

VENUS' CHARIOT
Aconitum napellus
Different subspecies of this western and central European plant are called Wolfsbane or Monkshood.

ROSES

This large family (Rosaceae) of around 2,000 species of woody trees, shrubs, climbers, and herbaceous plants is valued both for its bush and tree fruits and for many popular ornamentals. Distributed worldwide but with maximum variety in the temperate to subtropical zones of the Northern Hemisphere, roses are probably the most cultivated flowers in the world.

Fleshy fruits

Nectar-secreting disk

ELMLEAF BLACKBERRY
Rubus ulmifolius
A woody plant that propagates vegetatively by suckers and tip-roots.

Large, showy flowers

CINQUEFOIL
Potentilla argyrophylla
var. *atrosanguinea*
A herbaceous perennial, popular and widely cultivated.

JAPANESE ROSE
Kerria japonica
Petal multiplication is common in many ornamental cultivars

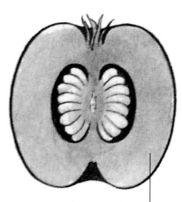

*Chaenomeles
speciosa fruit with
swollen receptacle*

*Alternate, simple
lanceolate leaves*

*Flower with
free carpels only
produces pollen*

ALPINE ROSE
Rosa pendulina
A woody shrub that bears
surface prickles and stipules
at the base of leaf stalks.

COTONEASTER
Cotoneaster salicifolius
This popularly cultivated
evergreen tree produces
bright red pomes.

*Common
Whitebeam
flowering shoot*

EUROPEAN PLUM
Prunus insititia
Grown extensively for
its fruits, which are
consumed fresh or
made into jams,
conserves, and liqueurs.

*Multiple
fleshy fruits*

CITRUS PLANTS AND COFFEES

Citrus fruits and coffees (Rutaceae and Rubiaceae) are some of the most important commercial crops in the world. Citrus trees have been cultivated for thousands of years, producing lemons, oranges, grapefruits, and other fruits.

Jungle Geranium tubular corolla opened out to show epipetalous stamens

Sarcocephalus pobeguinii vertical section of fruit

Vertical section of ovary

Coffea arabica *fruits*

JUNGLE GERANIUM
Ixora chinensis
Various *Ixora* species are found in tropical and subtropical areas across the world. They are members of the coffee family.

MUSSAENDA
Mussaenda species
Shown here displaying a flower with one calyx lobe much enlarged.

Sherbournia calycina
flowering shoot

*Sweet Orange
fruit is a hesperidium*

SWEET ORANGE
Citrus sinensis
One of numerous species of
orange, *Citrus aurantium* (Bitter
Orange) being another.

Yellow inflorescence

COMMON RUE
Ruta graveolens
This was once a
commonly used herb
but is now grown as a
garden ornamental.

LEMON
Citrus limon
Shown here is a
flowering shoot of
Lemon, now widely
cultivated but originally
a native of Asia.

WILLOWS, POPLARS, AND NORTH AMERICAN PITCHER PLANTS

Willows and poplars (Salicaceae) are common trees and shrubs in the Northern Hemisphere, from the Arctic to the tropics, but are poorly represented south of the equator. The carnivorous North American pitcher plants (Sarraceniaceae) form pitchers to trap insects, using a single rolled and modified leaf.

JAPANESE ASPEN
Populus sieboldii
Native to East Asia, Japanese Aspen grows quickly up to 66 feet (20 m) tall. It can be found throughout the mountains of Japan.

Japanese Aspen mature male catkins together with remains of one from previous year

Japanese Aspen shoot with cordate leaves

Shoot with young male catkin

Goat Willow young female catkin

Male catkin

GOAT WILLOW
Salix caprea
This deciduous tree is native to Europe and parts of Asia.

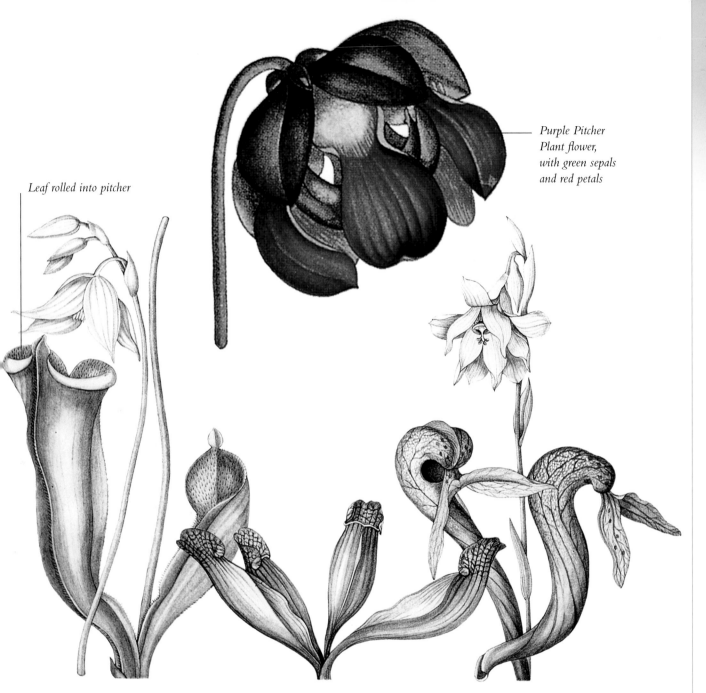

Leaf rolled into pitcher

Purple Pitcher Plant flower, with green sepals and red petals

HELIAMPHORA
Heliamphora nutans
Shown above are
Heliamphora's flowers
on leafless stalks. The
stamens, ovary, and style
are shown below.

PURPLE PITCHER PLANT
Sarracenia purpurea
This pitcher plant's distinctive
leaves are shown above. The
style and stigma of its flower
are seen below.

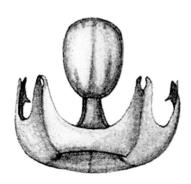

CALIFORNIA PITCHER PLANT
Darlingtonia californica
Pitchers and flowers are shown above.
A vertical section of the gynoecium,
showing stamens attached at the base,
is shown below.

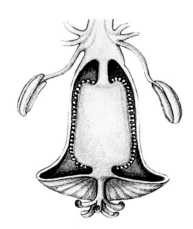

SOAPBERRIES
AND SAPODILLA

The soapberries (Sapindaceae) includes maples, horse chestnuts, and Lychee. Most species are woody climbers with pinnate leaves and unisexual flowers. Many produce edible fruits (lychee, rambutan, ackee) or valuable lumber. The Sapodilla is a member of the large Sapotaceae family of trees with latex in their twigs and fruit.

LYCHEE
Litchi chinensis
A tropical tree whose fruits are known for their edible arils (seed coverings).

Section through fruit

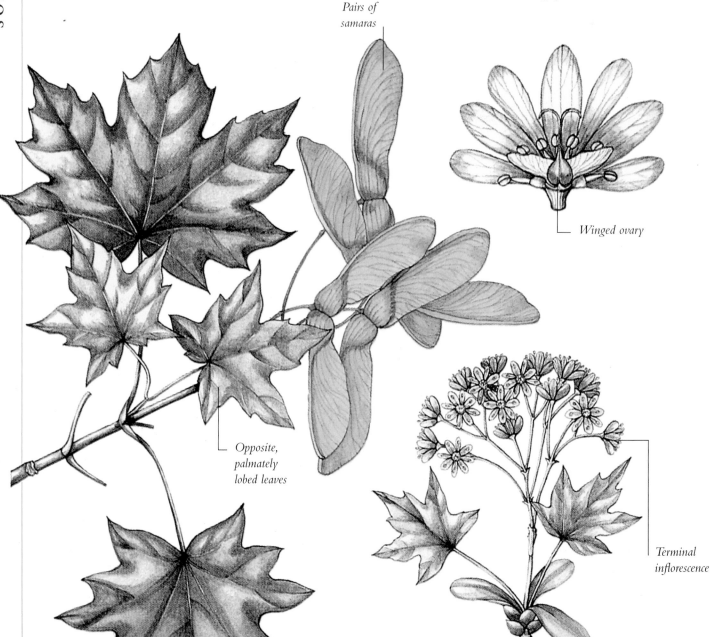

NORWAY MAPLE
Acer platanoides
This deciduous tree, native to Europe and West Asia, grows to 100 feet (30.5 m) tall.

Pairs of samaras

Winged ovary

Opposite, palmately lobed leaves

Terminal inflorescence

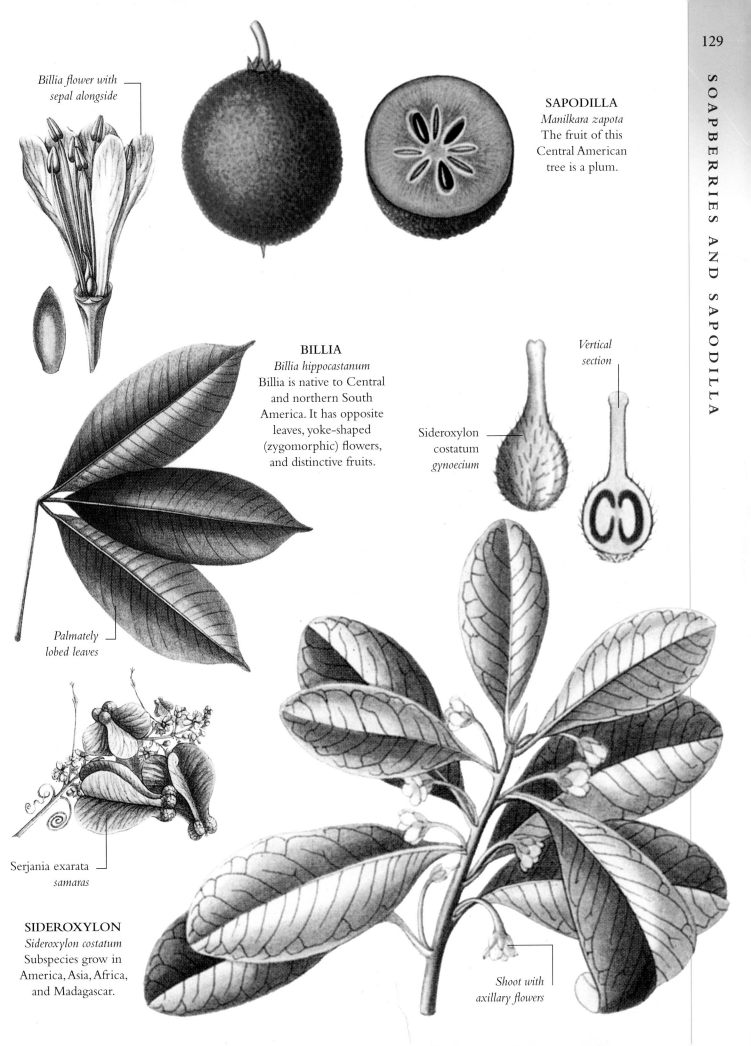

Billia flower with sepal alongside

SAPODILLA
Manilkara zapota
The fruit of this Central American tree is a plum.

BILLIA
Billia hippocastanum
Billia is native to Central and northern South America. It has opposite leaves, yoke-shaped (zygomorphic) flowers, and distinctive fruits.

Vertical section

Sideroxylon costatum *gynoecium*

Palmately lobed leaves

Serjania exarata *samaras*

SIDEROXYLON
Sideroxylon costatum
Subspecies grow in America, Asia, Africa, and Madagascar.

Shoot with axillary flowers

LIZARD'S TAILS
AND SAXIFRAGES

Lizard's tails (Saururaceae) are herbs with heart-shaped leaves and axillary spikelike inflorescences. There are just six species, in North America and East Asia. Saxifrages (Saxifragaceae) are primarily plants of the Northern Hemisphere, growing at high latitudes and high altitudes.

Cross section of inflorescence

Alternate, simple leaves with entire margins

YERBA MANSA
Anemopsis californica
One of two North American lizard's tails, this species grows between Washington State and western Mexico.

Flower lacks a perianth

Ovary sunk into its receptacle

GYMNOTHECA
Gymnotheca chinensis
Bears a narrow raceme of
inflorescence and alternate,
simple, heart-shaped
(cordate) leaves

INDIAN RHUBARB
Darmera peltata
Bears rounded leaves with the
stalk attached at the center.

Cordate leaves

SIBERIAN-TEA
Bergenia crassifolia
A herbaceous perennial
with spoon-shaped leaves.

*Vertical section
of ovary*

FIGWORTS AND FOXGLOVES

Figworts and foxgloves (Scrophulariaceae) are annual to perennial herbs, shrubs, or (rarely) lianas or trees. The family includes many commonly cultivated garden plants, such as *Digitalis*, *Penstemon*, and *Veronica*. There are representatives throughout the world, usually growing in open grassland but rarely in tropical forests. Extracts from some species have proved to be important medicinal drugs, with *Digitalis*, for example, a source of drugs used to treat heart disease.

Linaria vulgaris *half flower with spurred corolla and stamens of two lengths*

ALPINE BALSAM
Erinus alpinus
Shown below displaying a rosette of leaves and a terminal inflorescence of irregular flowers.

LITTLE YELLOW RATTLE
Rhinanthus minor
A semiparasitic plant that derives some of its nutrients from the roots of its neighbors.

Leaves are opposite

VERBASCUM
Verbascum betonicifolium
Seen here displaying its alternate leaves and an inflorescence of irregular flowers.

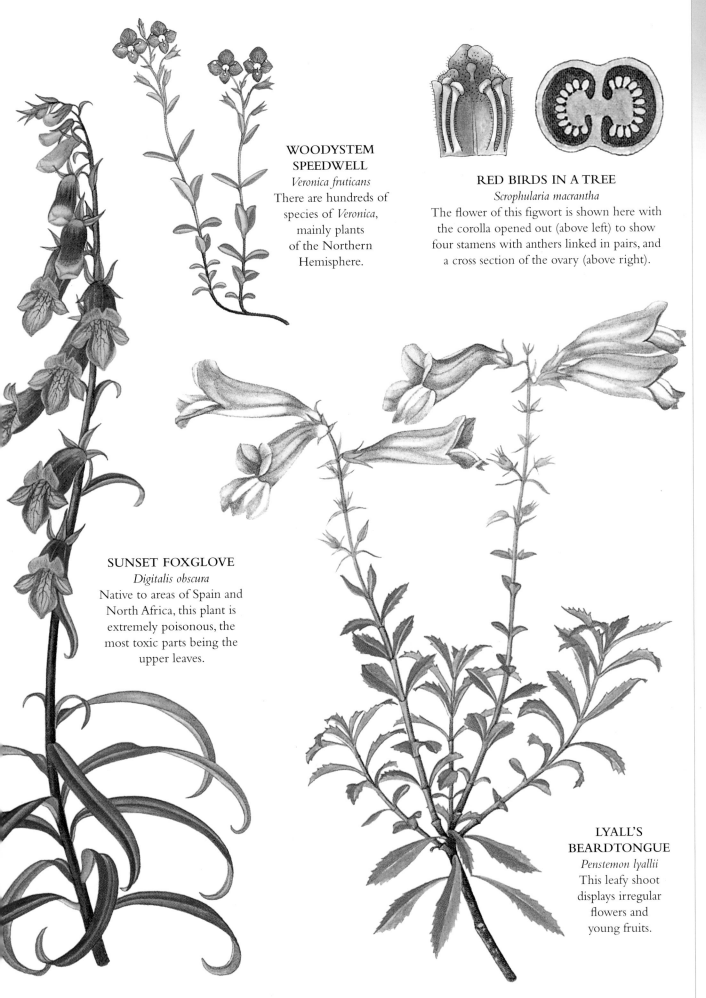

**WOODYSTEM
SPEEDWELL**
Veronica fruticans
There are hundreds of
species of *Veronica*,
mainly plants
of the Northern
Hemisphere.

RED BIRDS IN A TREE
Scrophularia macrantha
The flower of this figwort is shown here with
the corolla opened out (above left) to show
four stamens with anthers linked in pairs, and
a cross section of the ovary (above right).

SUNSET FOXGLOVE
Digitalis obscura
Native to areas of Spain and
North Africa, this plant is
extremely poisonous, the
most toxic parts being the
upper leaves.

**LYALL'S
BEARDTONGUE**
Penstemon lyallii
This leafy shoot
displays irregular
flowers and
young fruits.

POTATOES
AND BITTERWOOD

The potato family (Solanaceae) includes several important food crops, such as the potato and eggplant, as well as paprika, chilli pepper, cayenne, and bell pepper. It also includes Deadly Nightshade (*Atropa belladonna*) and Tobacco (*Nicotiana tabacum*), with its toxic alkaloid, nicotine. Bitterwood is part of the tropical family Simaroubaceae, a group of shrubs and large trees.

PAINTED TONGUE
Salpiglossis atropurpurea
Flowering shoot showing inflorescence with five-lobed, funnel-shaped corolla.

BITTERWOOD
Quassia amara
Extracts of Bitterwood bark, which is native to South America, make a natural insecticide.

Bitterwood calyx and gynoecium with disk at base

Bitterwood flower with petals removed to show numerous stamens

Bitterwood fruits

Fruit inside prickly calyx

Spines grow on the stems

Shoot with trifoliate leaves and inflorescence

Fruit in prickly calyx

JIMSONWEED
Datura stramonium
This foul-smelling North American herb has hallucinogenic properties and is highly toxic.

CHINESE LANTERN
Physalis alkekengi
Also known as Bladder Cherry, this plant grows from southern Europe across southern Asia to Japan.

Solanum rostratum
flower with two petals and two stamens removed

BUFFALO BUR NIGHTSHADE
Solanum rostratum
This annual herb forms a tumbleweed, breaking off near the base of the stem and scattering seeds as it moves around in the wind.

Fruits enclosed in persistent orange-red calyx

Paperlike calyx removed to show fruit

BLADDERNUTS AND TAMARISKS

Bladdernuts (Staphyleaceae) are large shrubs or trees. Evergreen trees in the genus *Turpinia* grow up to 115 feet (35 m) tall. Bladdernuts grow in many parts of the tropical and temperate zones. Tamarisks (Tamaricaceae) are generally small heathlike shrubs and small trees, usually with tiny pink or white flowers. The twigs of *Tamarisk manifera* yield a sweet substance known as *manna*, while other genera are a source of tannin, dyes, and medicinal extracts.

AFRICAN TAMARISK
Tamarix africana
This plant is often grown as an ornamental shrub for its feathery appearance and catkinlike inflorescences.

REAUMURIA
Reaumuria linifolia
A shrub native to the eastern Mediterranean and central Asia, with showy flowers.

Solitary terminal flowers

Trifoliate leaves

Axillary inflorescence

BLADDERNUT
Staphylea holocarpa
A deciduous shrub, endemic to northern temperate regions, but cultivated as an ornamental.

Staphylea holocarpa *flower*

Cross section of ovary

Dehiscing fruit

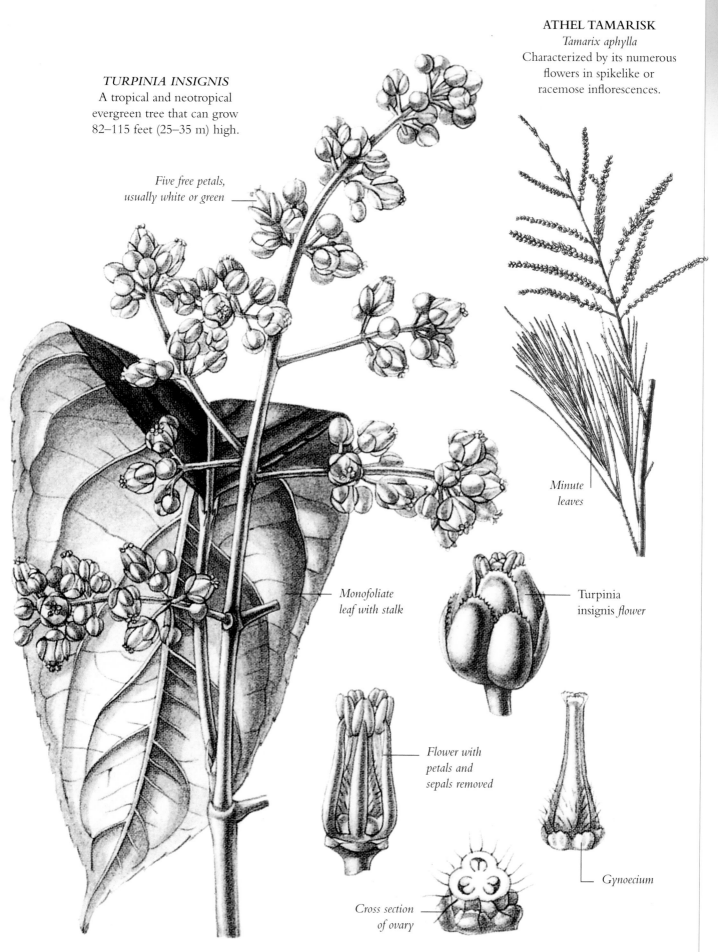

ATHEL TAMARISK
Tamarix aphylla
Characterized by its numerous flowers in spikelike or racemose inflorescences.

TURPINIA INSIGNIS
A tropical and neotropical evergreen tree that can grow 82–115 feet (25–35 m) high.

Five free petals, usually white or green

Monofoliate leaf with stalk

Minute leaves

Turpinia insignis *flower*

Flower with petals and sepals removed

Gynoecium

Cross section of ovary

TEAS, CAMELLIAS, AND DAPHNES

The family Theaceae is a relatively small group of trees and shrubs, usually with simple, evergreen leaves. The leaves of *Camellia sinensis* are brewed to make tea. Varieties of *C. sinensis* are extensively cultivated in India, Sri Lanka, China, and East Africa. The daphnes (Thymelaeaceae) are shrubs, trees, lianas, and herbs that have fibrous bark and phloem, giving the twigs and leaves toughness and flexibility.

CAMELLIA
Camellia rosiflora
A tropical or subtropical plant, which bears large, showy flowers.

Bright green, shiny leaves with hairs on the underside

Solitary flowers, borne in leaf axils

Tough, flexible leaf

Hypanthial cup with stamens

OCTOLEPIS
Octolepis flamignii
A member of the daphne family that bears simple, alternate fragrant leaves.

PARADISE PLANT
Daphne mezereum
This plant is often grown
as an ornamental because
of its fragrant flowers.

*Leafy shoot with
flowers and
flower buds*

*Daphne
mezereum
fruit—a berry*

*Terminal
inflorescences*

*Pimelea flower
showing
hyphanthium*

*Bright
red berries*

PIMELEA
Pimelea buxifolia
A daphne with fibrous bark.
This plant bears flowers with
one or two stamens.

Gynoecium

CAMELLIA
Camellia japonica
This shrub flowers from
January to mid-March, and
is sometimes referred to as
the "rose of winter."

*Half flower
with semi-
inferior ovary*

LIMES AND ELMS

The limes and lindens (Tiliaceae) are trees of warm-temperate regions in North America and Eurasia. They favor well-drained, lowland soils. Elms (Ulmaceae) grow more widely, with many species in South America, Africa, and Australia. These trees bear small apetalous flowers and winged or drupaceous fruits. Some genera have been depleted over recent decades by Dutch Elm disease.

Leafy shoot with flowers

ORIENTAL TREMA
Trema orientalis
A member of the elm family
with alternate, denticulate leaves.

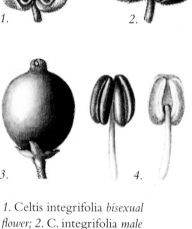

1. Celtis integrifolia *bisexual flower;* 2. C. integrifolia *male flower;* 3. Trema orientalis *fruit*
4. Ulmus campestris *anthers.*

1. Ulmus campestris *winged fruit*
2. U. campestris *gynoecium crowned by two styles*
3. U. campestris *flower with calyx and no petals*

ENGLISH ELM
Ulmus campestris
This tree was formerly a source of lumber, but stocks have been greatly depleted by Dutch Elm disease.

Cross section of fruit

Half flower

Simple leaves

PENDANT SILVER LINDEN
Tilia petiolaris
This was formerly an important source of wood for carving shields, bowls, toys, and frames.

Fruits with persistent bract

Serrate leaf margins

English Elm shoot with serrated leaf margins

LARGELEAF LINDEN
Tilia platyphyllos
This European deciduous tree grows to a height of 130 feet (39.6 m).

Fibrous bark

NASTURTIUMS
AND TURNERAS

Nasturtiums (Tropaeolaceae) make up a family of
climbing, fleshy herbs, native mainly to the Andes
Mountains of South America. Many are cultivated for
ornament, while the tubers of *Tropaeolum tuberosum* are
important root crops in the Andes. Turneras (Turneraceae)
are mainly tropical and subtropical shrubs and herbs,
which often bear showy yellow flowers. Some turneras
have medicinal properties.

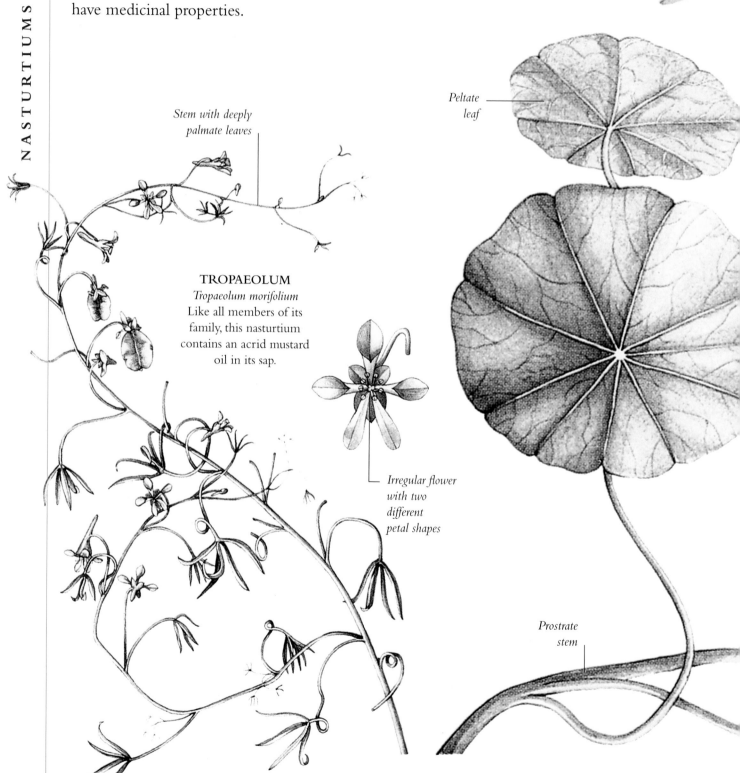

*Stem with deeply
palmate leaves*

**GARDEN
NASTURTIUM**
Tropaeolum majus
Often cultivated as
an ornamental, its
seeds are edible.

*Peltate
leaf*

TROPAEOLUM
Tropaeolum morifolium
Like all members of its
family, this nasturtium
contains an acrid mustard
oil in its sap.

*Irregular flower
with two
different
petal shapes*

*Prostrate
stem*

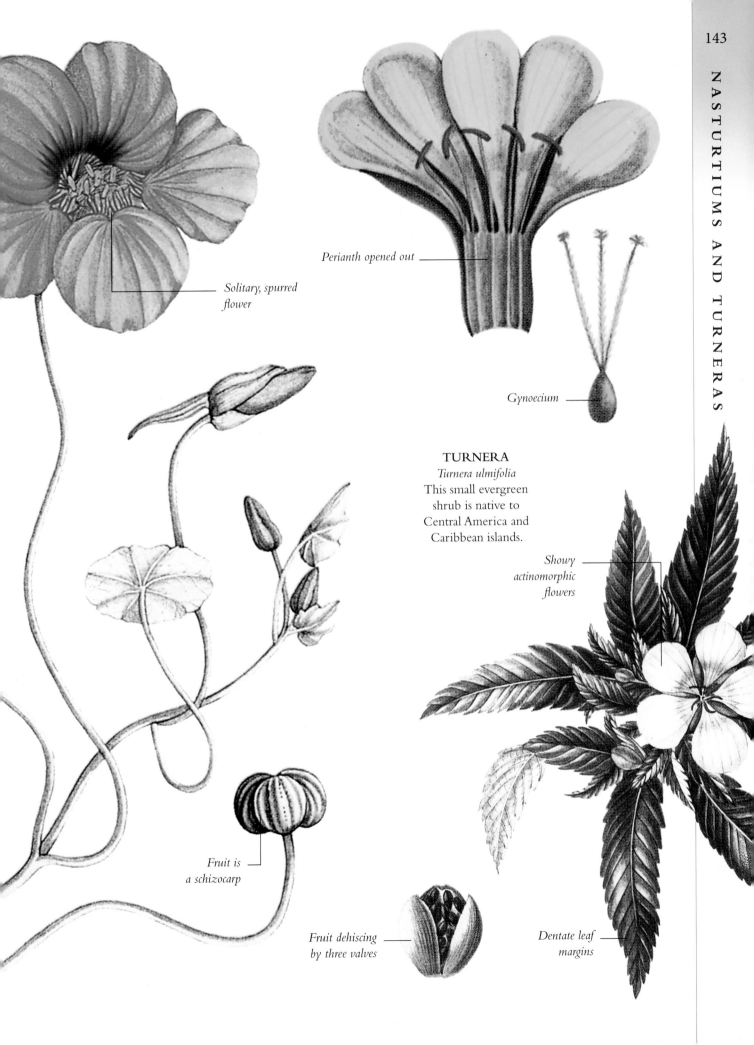

Solitary, spurred
flower

Perianth opened out

Gynoecium

TURNERA
Turnera ulmifolia
This small evergreen
shrub is native to
Central America and
Caribbean islands.

Showy
actinomorphic
flowers

Fruit is
a schizocarp

Fruit dehiscing
by three valves

Dentate leaf
margins

VALERIANS AND VIOLETS

Valerians (Valerianaceae) are annual to perennial herbs, sometimes woody at the base, which exhibit a great diversity of form. Some are edible, others are used in perfumery, and some have medicinal properties. Violets (Violaceae) are tropical trees, shrubs, vines, and lowland herbs, and temperate montane and alpine herbs (genus *Viola*).

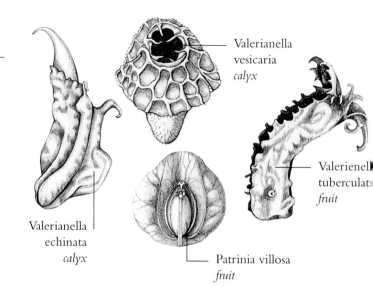

Valerianella
vesicaria
calyx

Valerienella
tuberculata
fruit

Valerianella
echinata
calyx

Patrinia villosa
fruit

MISCELLANEOUS VALERIANS

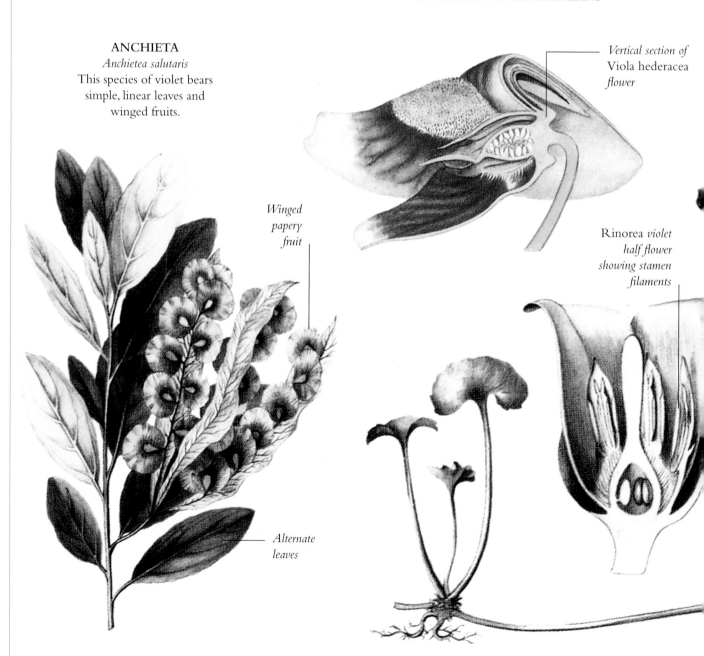

ANCHIETA
Anchietea salutaris
This species of violet bears simple, linear leaves and winged fruits.

Winged papery fruit

Alternate leaves

Vertical section of
Viola hederacea
flower

Rinorea *violet half flower showing stamen filaments*

TRAILING VIOLET
Viola hederacea
The leaves of this
herbaceous plant are
often used in
traditional medicine.

**MARSH
BLUE VIOLET**
Corynostylis arborea
A shoot and leaf
of this violet
(below) are shown.

Melicytus obovatus
leafy shoot with fruit

*Irregular
petals*

*Reniform
leaves*

CENTRANTHUS
Centranthus lecoqii
A Mediterranean valerian
that bears bright pink flowers
with distinctive spurs.

*Single stamen
and distinct spur*

*Valeriana
officinalis
flower*

146

GRAPEVINES
AND MISTLETOES

Grapevines (Vitaceae) have been cultivated for thousands of years for the production of table grapes, wine, fruit juice, and dried fruit (raisins, currants, and sultanas). Grapes for wine are now harvested all over the world from Canada and Kyrgyzstan to Chile and New Zealand. Mistletoes (Viscaceae) grow in tropical and temperate regions around the world. A traditional Christmas decoration in Europe and North America, it is not a climber like the vines, but a parasite that grows on other plants.

Grapevine inflorescence

Flower bud

Gynoecium

Flower with petals removed

Axillary inflorescence

TETRASTIGMA
Tetrastigma obtectum
This Asian and Australian climber is a member of the grapevine family.

GRAPE
Vitis thunbergii
This Asian grapevine displays a leaf with mature and immature fruits—grapes.

Cissus velutinus flower

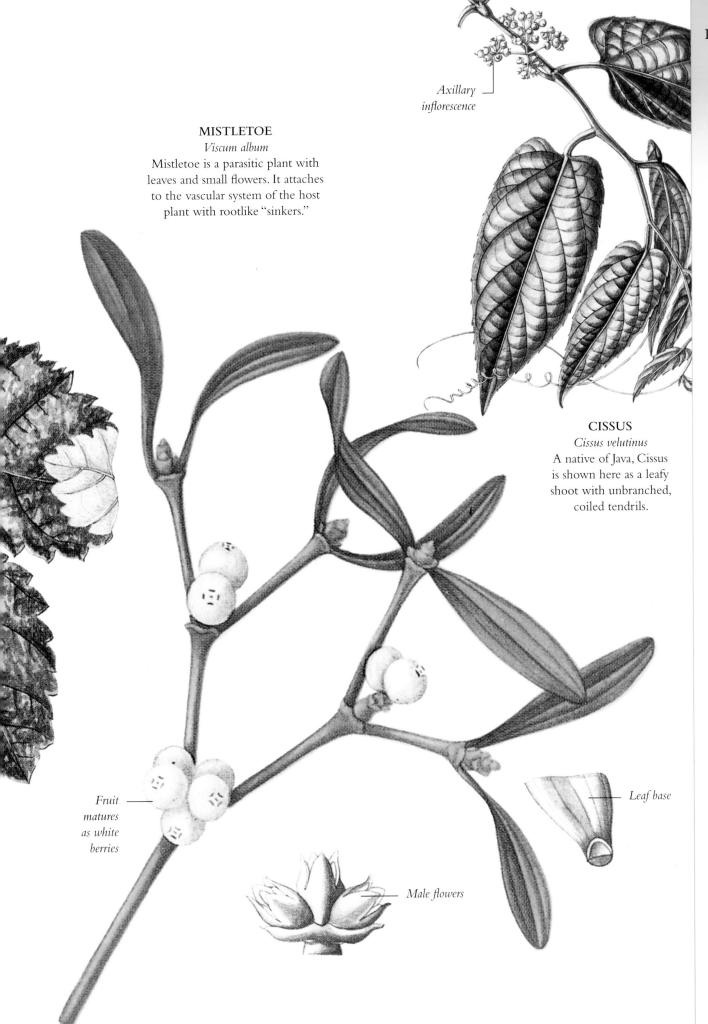

Axillary inflorescence

MISTLETOE
Viscum album
Mistletoe is a parasitic plant with leaves and small flowers. It attaches to the vascular system of the host plant with rootlike "sinkers."

CISSUS
Cissus velutinus
A native of Java, Cissus is shown here as a leafy shoot with unbranched, coiled tendrils.

Fruit matures as white berries

Leaf base

Male flowers

VOCHYSIACEAE
AND WINTER'S BARKS

A small family of medium to large trees, growing mostly
in South America, Vochysiaceae species have attractive
and distinctive flowers. Winter's barks (Winteraceae) are
aromatic evergreen trees or shrubs, whose wood lacks
vessels. These plants grow mainly in montane or cool
temperate rain forests.

Winged fruit

***VOCHYSIA
DIVERGENS***
A tree with opposite,
simple leaves and
terminal, racemose
inflorescences.

*Single
petal*

*Simple leaf
margins*

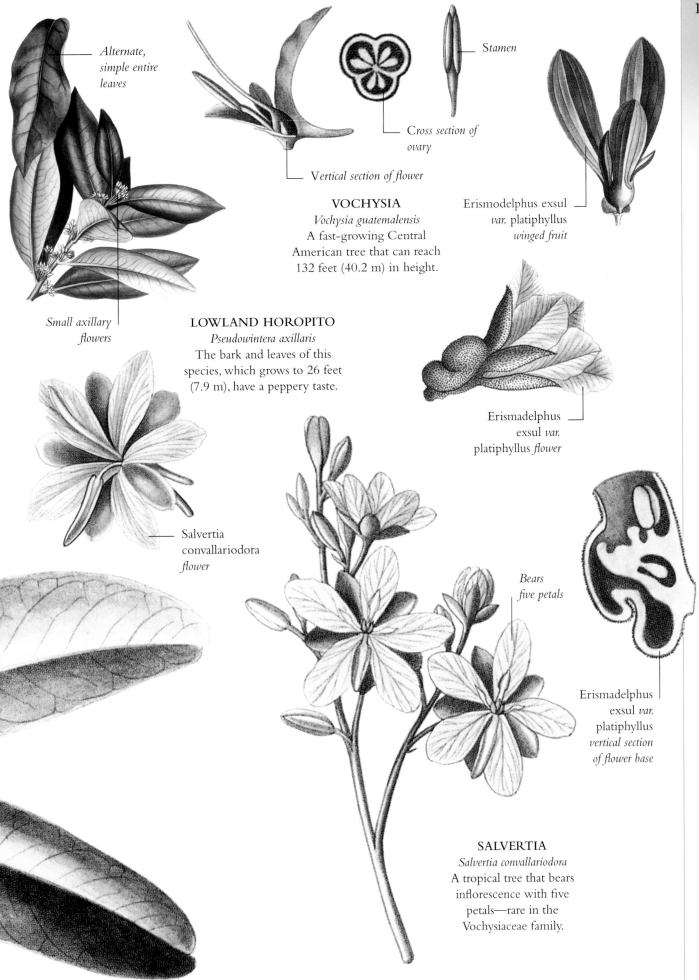

Alternate, simple entire leaves

Stamen

Cross section of ovary

Vertical section of flower

Erismodelphus exsul *var.* platiphyllus *winged fruit*

VOCHYSIA
Vochysia guatemalensis
A fast-growing Central
American tree that can reach
132 feet (40.2 m) in height.

Small axillary flowers

LOWLAND HOROPITO
Pseudowintera axillaris
The bark and leaves of this
species, which grows to 26 feet
(7.9 m), have a peppery taste.

Erismadelphus
exsul *var.*
platiphyllus *flower*

Salvertia
convallariodora
flower

*Bears
five petals*

Erismadelphus
exsul *var.*
platiphyllus
*vertical section
of flower base*

SALVERTIA
Salvertia convallariodora
A tropical tree that bears
inflorescence with five
petals—rare in the
Vochysiaceae family.

DAFFODILS
AND ONIONS

Most daffodils (Amaryllidaceae) are bulbous, perennial herbs, but some are aquatics or epiphytes. The flower or flowers are often large and showy. Some daffodils are popular ornamentals. There are up to 750 species of bulbous or rhizomatous herbs in the onion family (Alliaceae), some of which are used to flavor food. Onions, chives, and leeks are all members of the family.

FLOWERING ONION
Allium cyaneum
A species of Alliaceae that is often cultivated as a garden ornamental.

Terete leaves

Rhizome root structure

Fruit is a berry

BUSH LILY
Clivia miniata
This member of the daffodil family is adapted for life in seasonally dry environments.

Umbel-like inflorescence

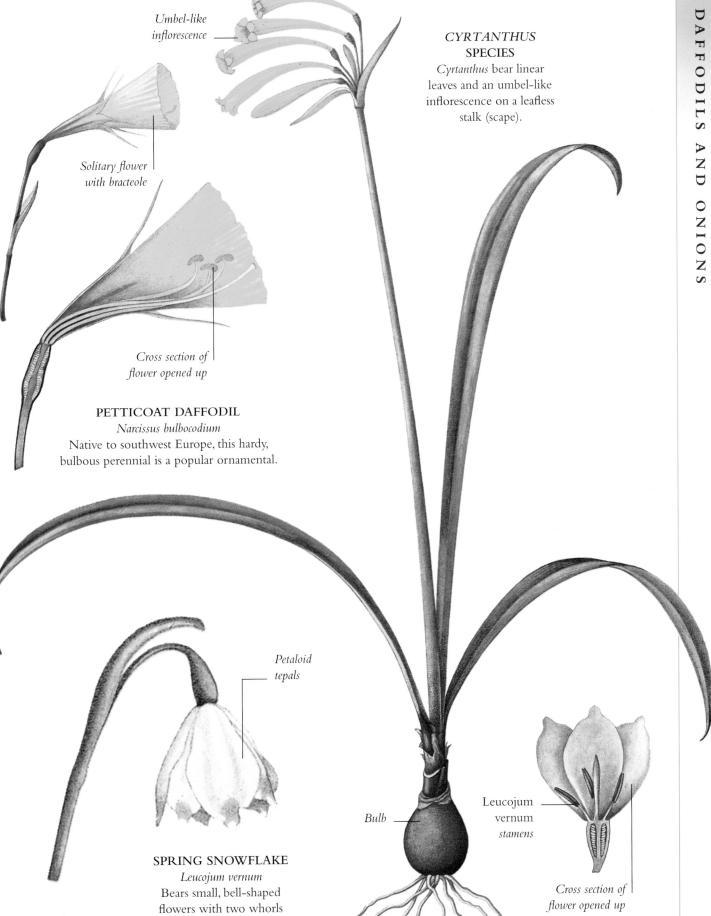

Umbel-like
inflorescence

CYRTANTHUS
SPECIES
Cyrtanthus bear linear
leaves and an umbel-like
inflorescence on a leafless
stalk (scape).

Solitary flower
with bracteole

Cross section of
flower opened up

PETTICOAT DAFFODIL
Narcissus bulbocodium
Native to southwest Europe, this hardy,
bulbous perennial is a popular ornamental.

Petaloid
tepals

Bulb

Leucojum
vernum
stamens

SPRING SNOWFLAKE
Leucojum vernum
Bears small, bell-shaped
flowers with two whorls
of free perianth segments.

Cross section of
flower opened up

DUCKWEEDS AND WATER HAWTHORNS

Duckweeds (Araceae) form a family of minute floating aquatic herbs with reduced flowers that grow worldwide (apart from in arid regions). Many have edible tubers or stems. Water hawthorns (Aponogetonaceae) make up a single genus of rhizomatous or aquatic plants with a spiked inflorescence. They are generally restricted to warm and tropical environments.

Lemna gibba
cross section of fruit

Lemna minor
opened fruit with seed

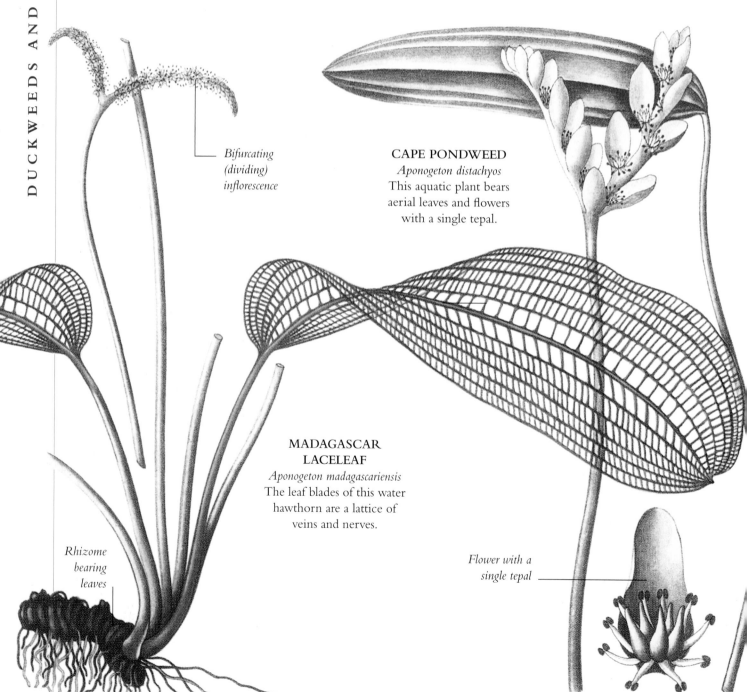

Bifurcating (dividing) inflorescence

CAPE PONDWEED
Aponogeton distachyos
This aquatic plant bears aerial leaves and flowers with a single tepal.

MADAGASCAR LACELEAF
Aponogeton madagascariensis
The leaf blades of this water hawthorn are a lattice of veins and nerves.

Rhizome bearing leaves

Flower with a single tepal

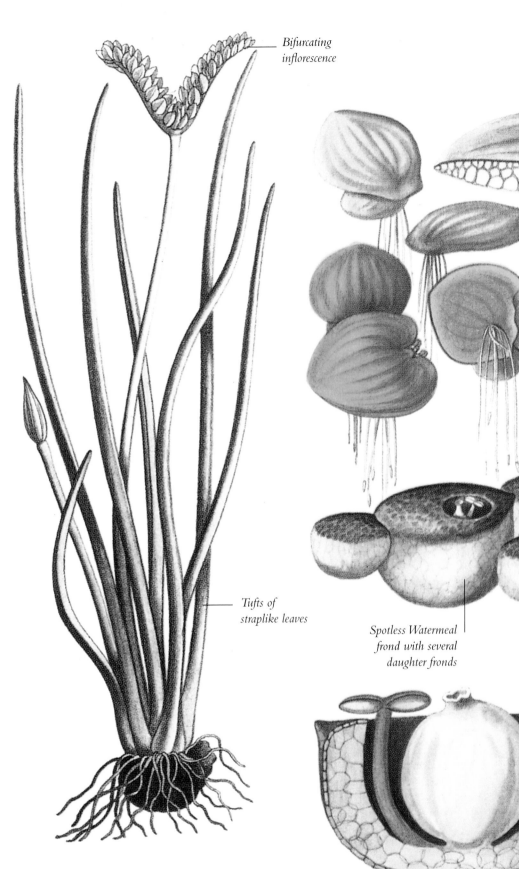

*Bifurcating
inflorescence*

*Greater Duckweed
fronds with
prominent roots*

*Tufts of
straplike leaves*

*Spotless Watermeal
frond with several
daughter fronds*

*Section of frond
with daughter
frond budding off*

APONOGETON
Aponogeton junceus
This water hawthorn has
tuberlike corms, small
leaves, and bifurcating
inflorescence.

SPOTLESS WATERMEAL
Wolffia arrhiza
Bears small flowers within a
recessed cavity and lacks roots.

PALMS

Palms (Arecaceae) are tree- or shrublike plants or lianas, with woody stems and often large, tough leaves. They also have axillary inflorescences, numerous flowers, and single-seed fruits. Palms grow mainly in the tropics. The family is of immense economic importance, with palm products used in foods, medicines, and cosmetics.

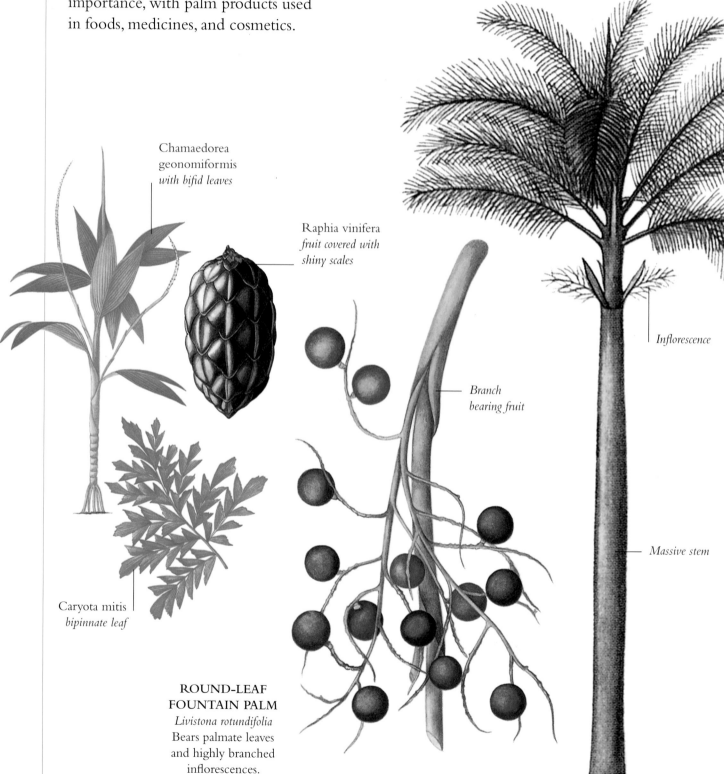

ROYAL PALM
Roystonea regia
The inflorescence of this palm appears below the crown.

Chamaedorea geonomiformis *with bifid leaves*

Raphia vinifera *fruit covered with shiny scales*

Caryota mitis *bipinnate leaf*

Branch bearing fruit

Inflorescence

Massive stem

ROUND-LEAF FOUNTAIN PALM
Livistona rotundifolia
Bears palmate leaves and highly branched inflorescences.

Chamaedorea
fragrans *male
inflorescence*

Caryota cumingii
*male flower with
three sepals and
three petals*

Caryota
cumingii
*open male
flower*

Elaeis
guineensis
*vertical
section
of fruit*

*Massive
terminal
inflorescence*

TALIPOT PALM
Corypha umbraculifera
This species bears
treelike inflorescences
that can have millions
of flowers.

DOUM PALM
Hyphaene thebaica
This species develops
dichotomous branching,
unusual for a palm.

Arenga
westerhoutii
*vertical section
of fruit*

Arenga
westerhoutii
*fruit with
perianth remains*

*Dichotomous
branching*

ALOES AND BROMELIADS

Aloes (Asphodelaceae) are predominantly herbs with succulent leaves in basal or terminal rosettes. They are widespread in temperate, subtropical, and tropical regions of the Old World. Bromeliads (Bromeliaceae) are frequently epiphytic, rosette plants, almost exclusively native to the Americas. *Ananas comosus* (pineapple) is an important edible fruit within this family.

Inflorescence with showy bracts

PAINTED FEATHER
Vriesea carinata
A herbaceous epiphyte that bears spirally arranged, evergreen leaves.

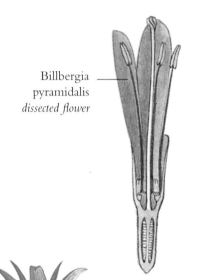

Billbergia
pyramidalis
dissected flower

PINEAPPLE
Ananas comosus
The edible, multiple fruit is produced from the entire inflorescence.

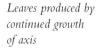

Leaves produced by continued growth of axis

Inflorescence borne on well-developed peduncle

FOOLPROOF PLANT
Billbergia pyramidalis
Bears leaves with spiny margins and inflorescence with large red bracts.

ALOE
Aloe jucunda
Bears a basal rosette of spiny, fleshy leaves and raceme inflorescence.

Inflorescence with reduced bracts

Unexpanded leaf-bases

PITCAIRNIA
Pitcairnia integrifolia
A terrestrial species of bromeliad, which has a fully developed root system.

Large showy bracts

NAKED STEM LIVING VASE
Aechmea nudicaulis
Cultivated as an ornamental for its vibrant inflorescence.

BURMANNIAS AND CANNAS

The burmannias (Burmanniaceae) are mostly small herbs, which are often tinted reddish, yellowish, or white. Some members of the family lack chlorophyll and live symbiotically with fungi. Cannas (Cannaceae) are large, rhizomatous herbs with large, attractive, asymmetric flowers. They are native to the tropics and subtropics of the New World.

Monochasial inflorescence

Flowers with winged perianth tubes

Perianth opened out showing six tepals

Scale-like leaves

Cross section through flower, showing pendant stamens

INDIAN BLUETHREAD
Burmannia coelestis
An annual herb growing 2–6 inches (5–15 cm) tall, the flowers arise singly or with three together.

Tuberous rhizome

HAPLOTHISMIA EXANNULATA
This plant is endemic to Malabar high-altitude evergreen forest in southern India and grows on decaying organic matter.

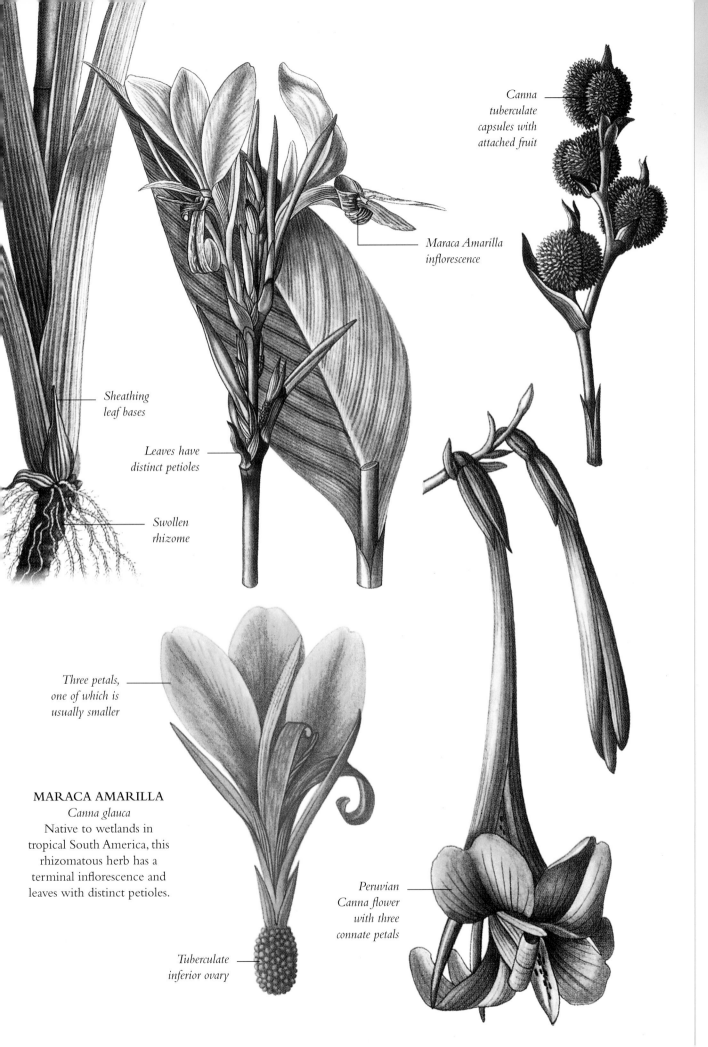

Canna tuberculate capsules with attached fruit

Maraca Amarilla inflorescence

Sheathing leaf bases

Leaves have distinct petioles

Swollen rhizome

Three petals, one of which is usually smaller

MARACA AMARILLA
Canna glauca
Native to wetlands in tropical South America, this rhizomatous herb has a terminal inflorescence and leaves with distinct petioles.

Peruvian Canna flower with three connate petals

Tuberculate inferior ovary

COLCHICUMS
AND SPIDERWORTS

Colchicums (Colchicaceae) are perennials with underground corms or rhizomes; they often have large flowers. Representatives typically grow in areas with a Mediterranean climate. Most spiderworts (Commelinaceae) are perennial herbs of the tropics, but some grow in temperate regions. Their flowers lack nectar—pollen is the only reward for their pollinators. Some species have rhizomes.

INCH PLANT
Tradescantia zebrina
One of the rhizomatous spiderworts, this plant has subtly striped leaves.

Slender Dayflower shoot with sheathing leaf bases

Spirally arranged leaves

Leaves wth sheathed bases

GIBASIS GRAMINIFOLIA
This spiderwort typically grows in grasslands and forests in humid conditions.

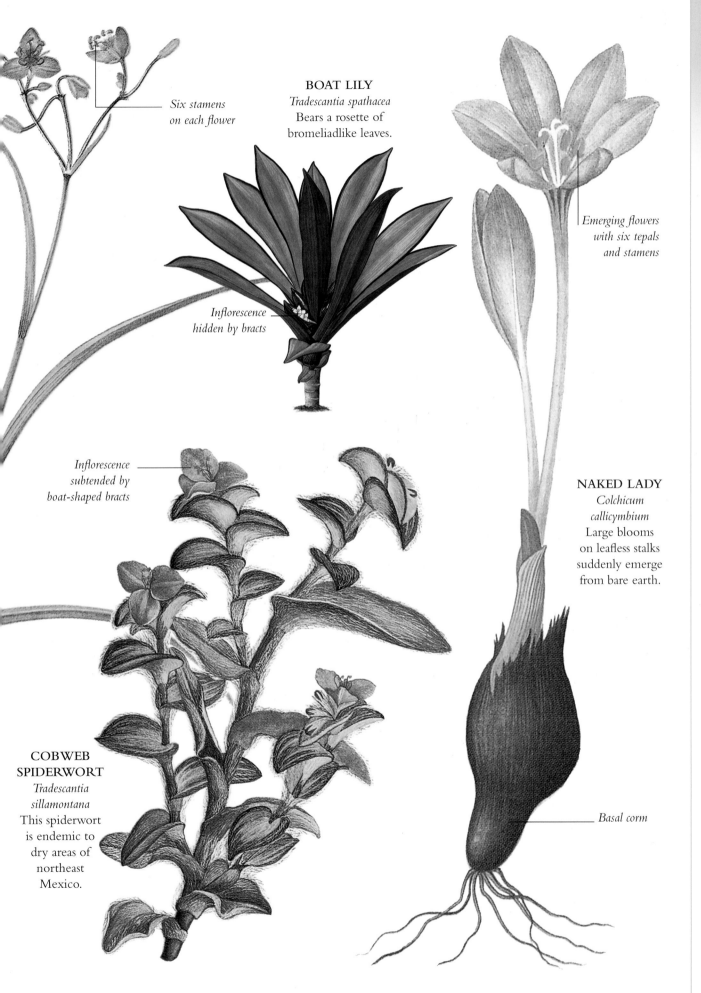

*Six stamens
on each flower*

BOAT LILY
Tradescantia spathacea
Bears a rosette of
bromeliadlike leaves.

*Emerging flowers
with six tepals
and stamens*

*Inflorescence
hidden by bracts*

*Inflorescence
subtended by
boat-shaped bracts*

NAKED LADY
*Colchicum
callicymbium*
Large blooms
on leafless stalks
suddenly emerge
from bare earth.

**COBWEB
SPIDERWORT**
*Tradescantia
sillamontana*
This spiderwort
is endemic to
dry areas of
northeast
Mexico.

Basal corm

COSTUS AND PANAMA HATS

The costus (Costaceae) are rhizomatous herbs, with simple leaves and often with brightly colored bracts and flowers. Most species are confined to lowland or montane humid tropical forests. The Panama hat family (Cyclanthaceae) is made up of perennial epiphytes, root-climbers, and terrestrial herbs, with alternate, simple leaves. The family is economically important for *Carludovica palmata*, the leaves and fibers of which are woven into Panama hats.

PANAMA HAT PLANT
Carludovica rotundifolia
Bears an inflorescence with connate female flowers and fleshy orange fruits.

Fleshy orange fruits

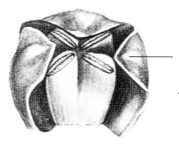

Stelestylis stylaris *female flower*

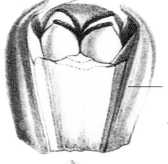

Evodianthus funifer *young fruit*

Evodianthus funifer *male flower*

EVIODANTHUS FUNIFER
Eviodanthus is a species of Panama hat plant that grows on some Caribbean islands and in northern South America.

Fanlike leaves

Fused female flowers

Evodianthus funifer *half male flower in bud*

Asplundia vagans *(a Panama hat) with lateral inflorescence*

Cyclanthus bipartitus *(a Panama hat) tip of spadix*

Female flower with long staminodes

COSTUS
Costus afer
A monoecious plant that bears alternate simple leaves and a basal ligule.

Young fruit inside tepals

Globelike inflorescence

SEDGES

Sedges (Cyperaceae) grow on every continent apart from Antarctica. They are especially abundant in damp, wet, or marshy areas of the temperate and subarctic zones, where they may be the dominant plants. Most of the 4,500 or so species of sedges are perennial, grasslike herbs.

Inflorescences are male and female spikelets

CAREX DECURTATA
This perennial rhizomatous herb has basal leaves and terminal inflorescences with spikelets of unisexual flowers.

Cladium tetraquetrum *inflorescence*

Male spikelet

Female spikelet

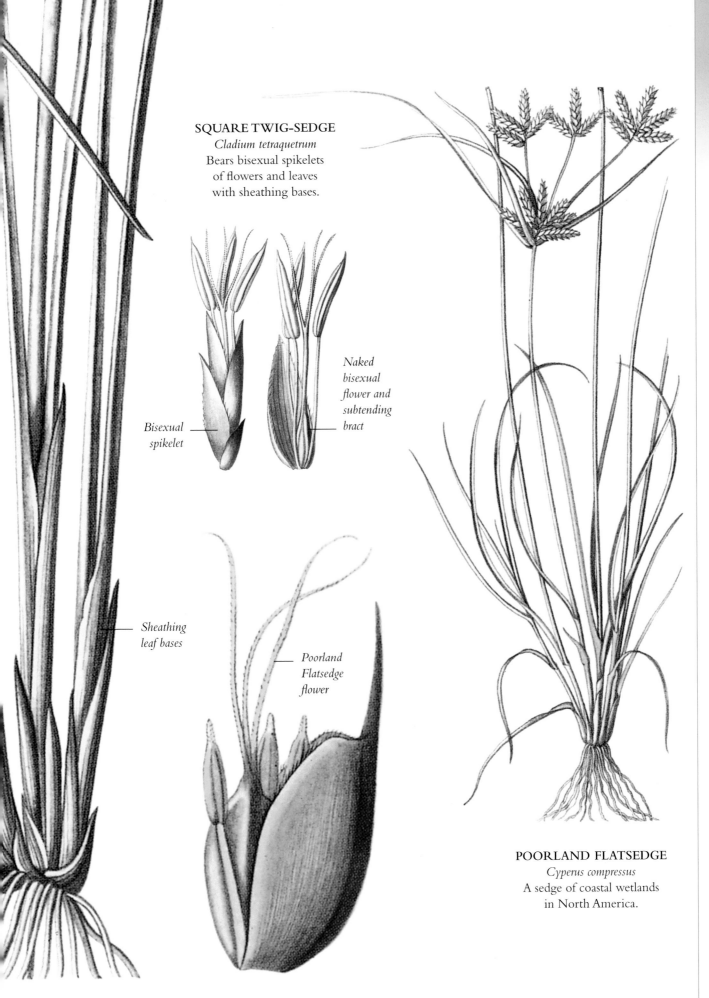

SQUARE TWIG-SEDGE
Cladium tetraquetrum
Bears bisexual spikelets
of flowers and leaves
with sheathing bases.

*Naked
bisexual
flower and
subtending
bract*

*Bisexual
spikelet*

*Sheathing
leaf bases*

*Poorland
Flatsedge
flower*

POORLAND FLATSEDGE
Cyperus compressus
A sedge of coastal wetlands
in North America.

PIPEWORTS AND FLAGELLARIAS

PIPEWORTS
AND FLAGELLARIAS

Pipeworts (Eriocaulaceae) are mainly tropical herbs, often with the spirally aranged leaves forming dense rosettes and bearing characteristic head- or buttonlike inflorescences on the ends of long leafless peduncles. There are just four species of flagellarias (Flagellariaceae)—climbing or scrambling tropical lianas.

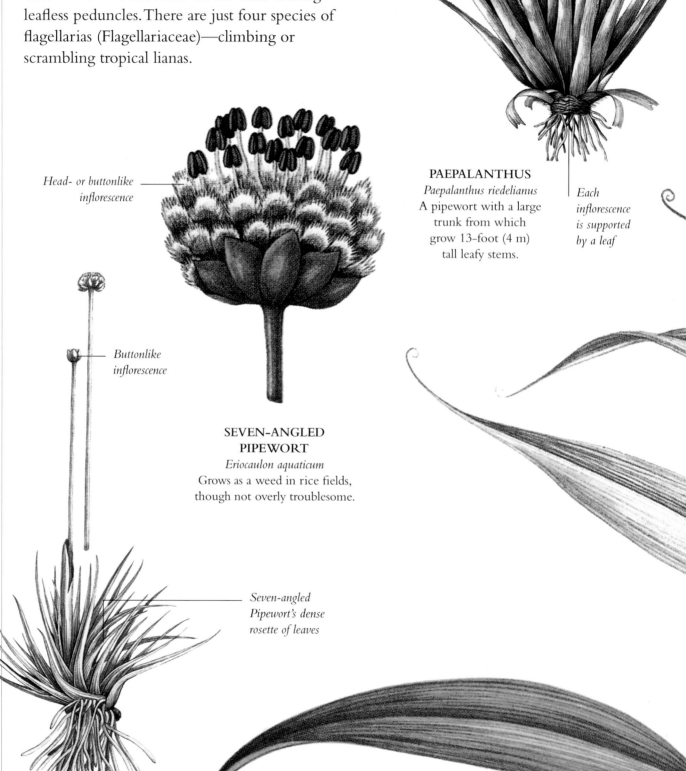

Head- or buttonlike
inflorescence

Buttonlike
inflorescence

PAEPALANTHUS
Paepalanthus riedelianus
A pipewort with a large
trunk from which
grow 13-foot (4 m)
tall leafy stems.

*Each
inflorescence
is supported
by a leaf*

**SEVEN-ANGLED
PIPEWORT**
Eriocaulon aquaticum
Grows as a weed in rice fields,
though not overly troublesome.

*Seven-angled
Pipewort's dense
rosette of leaves*

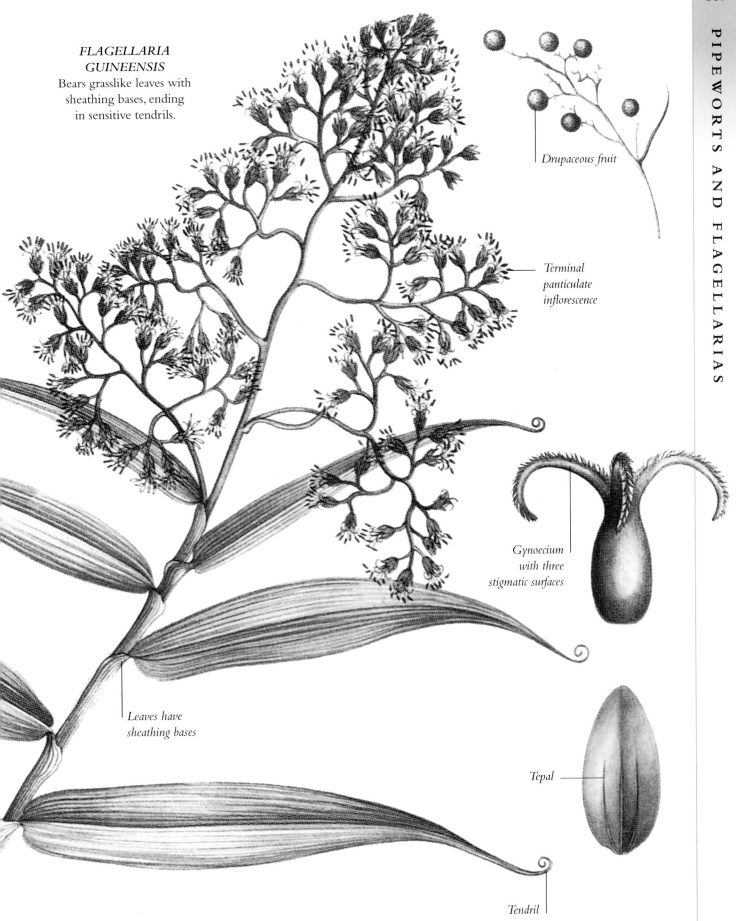

FLAGELLARIA GUINEENSIS
Bears grasslike leaves with sheathing bases, ending in sensitive tendrils.

Drupaceous fruit

Terminal paniculate inflorescence

Gynoecium with three stigmatic surfaces

Leaves have sheathing bases

Tepal

Tendril

BLOODWORTS AND FROG-BITS

Bloodworts (Haemodoraceae) are perennial herbs
with rhizomes, corms, or bulbs, which are often—like
the roots—red or reddish. They grow in temperate and
tropical areas of Australia, northern South America, the
Atlantic coast of North America, and South Africa.
Frog-bits (Hydrocharitaceae) are freshwater and
marine aquatics, often regarded as invasive nuisances.

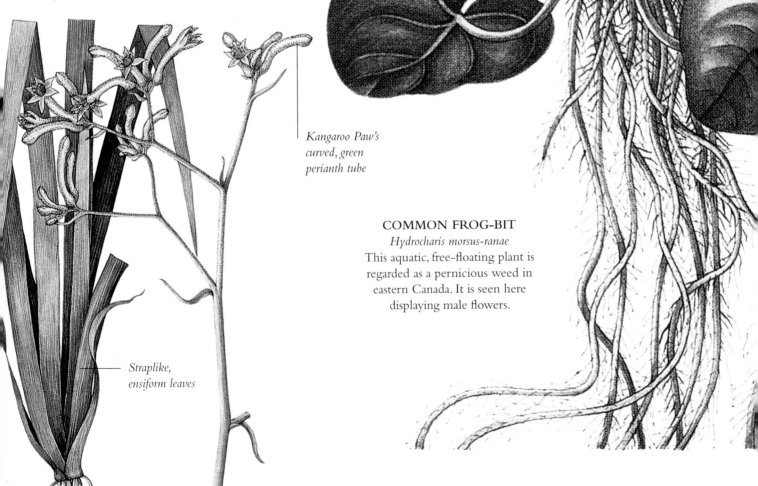

**EVERGREEN
KANGAROO PAW**
Anigozanthos flavidus
This perennial bloodwort from
southwest Australia grows near
creeks, in swamps, and in other
damp, unshaded habitats.

*Leaves
float on
surface of
water*

*Kangaroo Paw's
curved, green
perianth tube*

COMMON FROG-BIT
Hydrocharis morsus-ranae
This aquatic, free-floating plant is
regarded as a pernicious weed in
eastern Canada. It is seen here
displaying male flowers.

*Straplike,
ensiform leaves*

1. Elodea canadensis *female flower with three forked styles*
2. Hydrocharis morsus-ranae *female flower*
3. Hydrocharis morsus-ranae *cross section of fruit*
4. Phlebocarya ciliata *vertical section of ovary*

1.   *2.*   *3.*   *4.*

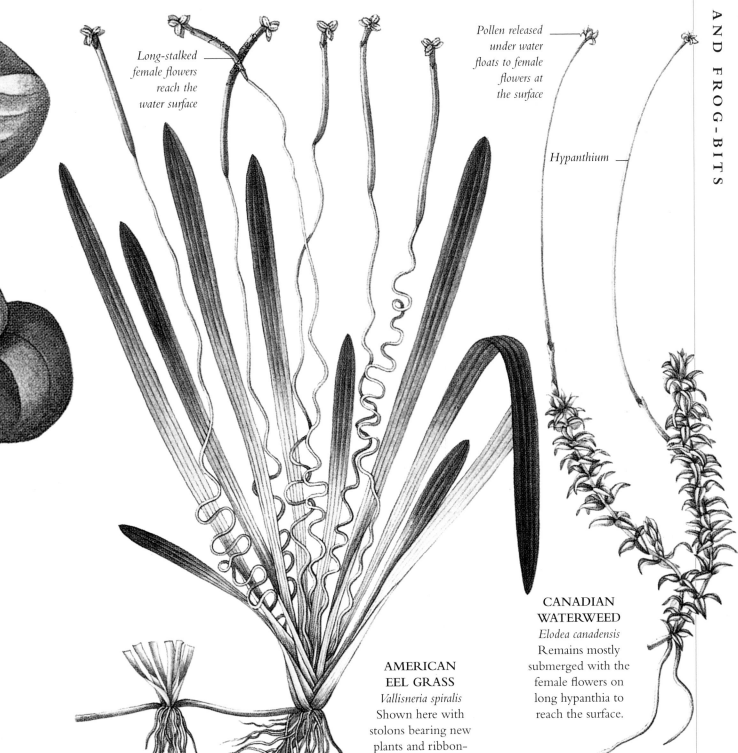

Long-stalked female flowers reach the water surface

Pollen released under water floats to female flowers at the surface

Hypanthium

AMERICAN EEL GRASS
Vallisneria spiralis
Shown here with stolons bearing new plants and ribbon-shaped leaves.

CANADIAN WATERWEED
Elodea canadensis
Remains mostly submerged with the female flowers on long hypanthia to reach the surface.

IRISES AND PHILESIAS

Irises (Iridaceae) thrive in both tropical and temperate zones, with South Africa and Central and South America especially rich in species. Most irises grow in open scrub, deserts, and grassland, but the family is conspicuously absent from South Asia, the Sahara Desert, and the interior of Australia. *Crocus sativus* provides the spice saffron. The two species of philesia (Philesiaceae) grow exclusively in the forests of southern Chile.

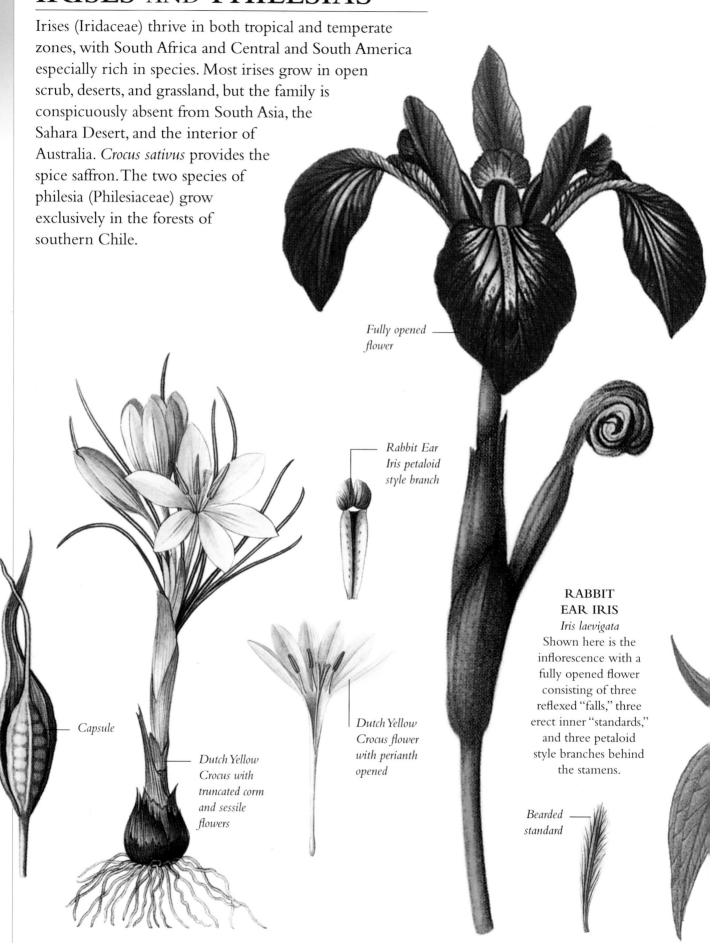

Fully opened flower

Rabbit Ear Iris petaloid style branch

Capsule

Dutch Yellow Crocus with truncated corm and sessile flowers

Dutch Yellow Crocus flower with perianth opened

RABBIT EAR IRIS
Iris laevigata
Shown here is the inflorescence with a fully opened flower consisting of three reflexed "falls," three erect inner "standards," and three petaloid style branches behind the stamens.

Bearded standard

Stinking Iris dehiscing capsule with seeds

Spotted tepals

Butterfly Sword Lily spiked inflorescence

CHILEAN BELLFLOWER
Lapageria rosea
One of two species of philesia, found only in Chile, this twining, leafy plant displays solitary axillary flowers.

Rabbit Ear Iris apex of rhizome and leaf bases of ensiform leaves

PRAYER PLANTS AND ARROWGRASSES

Prayer plants (Marantaceae) are herbaceous perennials with underground rhizomes or tubers. They grow in tropical regions of Central and South America, Africa, and Asia. Arrowgrasses (Juncaginaceae) are rhizomatous marsh herbs with basal leaves and inconspicuous flowers. Their greatest diversity is found in temperate regions.

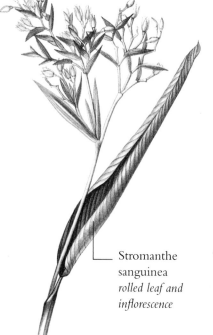

Luzula
alpinopilosa
ovary

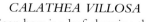

CALATHEA VILLOSA
Seen here is a leaf, showing the basal sheath, and the simple inflorescence with flowers subtended by green bracts.

Stromanthe
sanguinea
rolled leaf and inflorescence

Maranta Arrowroot
shoot with leaves and inflorescence

TOAD RUSH
Juncus bufonius
Here (right) showing erect linear leaves with loosely sheathing bases and dense flowers in cymose heads.

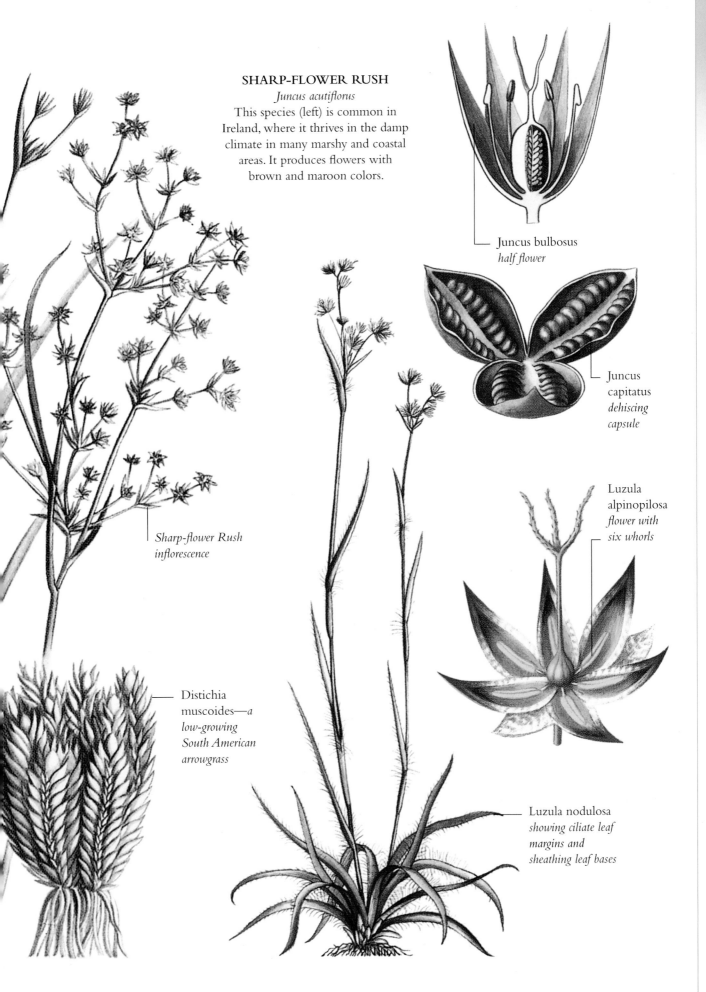

SHARP-FLOWER RUSH
Juncus acutiflorus
This species (left) is common in
Ireland, where it thrives in the damp
climate in many marshy and coastal
areas. It produces flowers with
brown and maroon colors.

Juncus bulbosus
half flower

Juncus
capitatus
*dehiscing
capsule*

*Sharp-flower Rush
inflorescence*

Luzula
alpinopilosa
*flower with
six whorls*

Distichia
muscoides—*a
low-growing
South American
arrowgrass*

Luzula nodulosa
*showing ciliate leaf
margins and
sheathing leaf bases*

BANANAS AND LILIES

The banana family (Musaceae) provides one of the world's major food crops. These plants are large to gigantic herbs, with pseudostems formed of overlapping sheaths. They grow mostly in wet, tropical lowlands. Lilies (Liliaceae), famed for their flowers, are mostly plants of the temperate Northern Hemisphere.

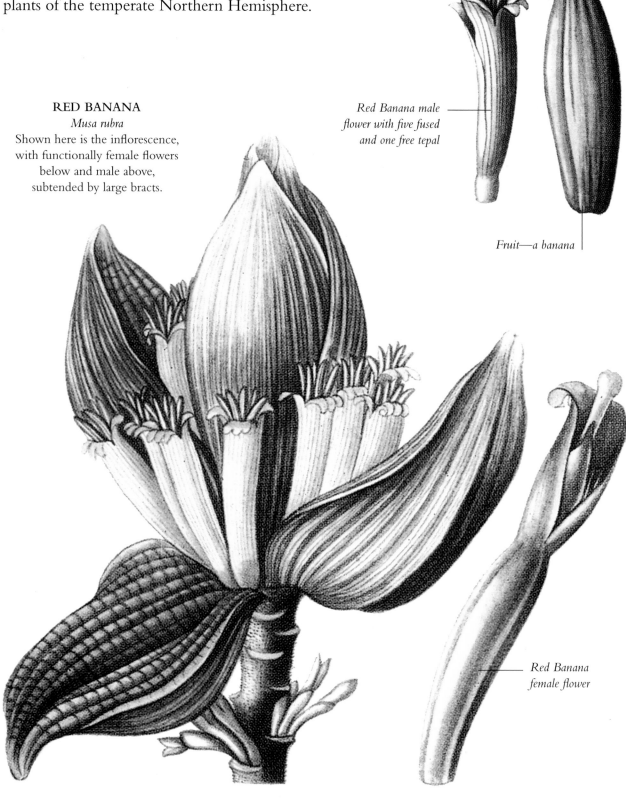

RED BANANA
Musa rubra
Shown here is the inflorescence, with functionally female flowers below and male above, subtended by large bracts.

Red Banana male flower with five fused and one free tepal

Fruit—a banana

Red Banana female flower

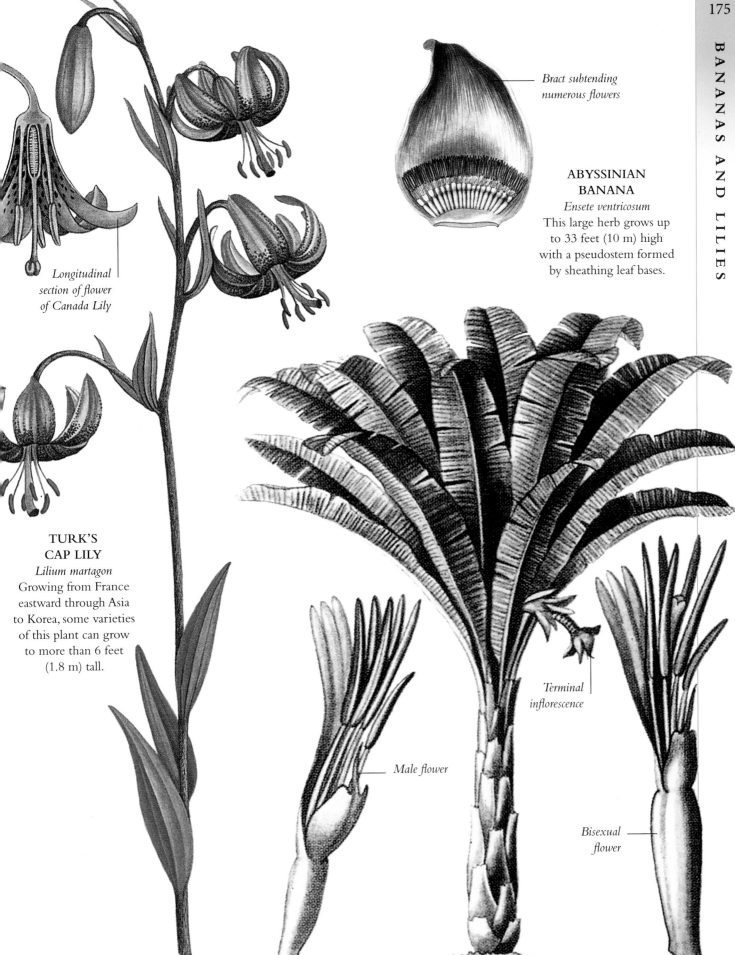

Bract subtending
numerous flowers

ABYSSINIAN BANANA
Ensete ventricosum
This large herb grows up
to 33 feet (10 m) high
with a pseudostem formed
by sheathing leaf bases.

Longitudinal
section of flower
of Canada Lily

TURK'S CAP LILY
Lilium martagon
Growing from France
eastward through Asia
to Korea, some varieties
of this plant can grow
to more than 6 feet
(1.8 m) tall.

Male flower

Terminal
inflorescence

Bisexual
flower

ORCHIDS

Orchids (Orchidaceae) make up the largest family of flowering plants, up to 20,000 species in total. They are characterized by their often showy, strongly zygomorphic flowers and numerous dustlike seeds. Orchids grow as understory plants in dark, tropical forests; at the top of tall trees in rain forests, where they are exposed to sunshine and showered by torrential rain; and in grassy and marshy areas. They are only absent from the driest deserts, the coldest mountains, and the Arctic.

CHARMING DENDROBIUM
Dendrobium pulchellum
This Southeast Asian orchid has a creeping stem and spotted leaves.

SOPHRONITIS COCCINEA
A South American species, this orchid is native to Brazil and Argentina.

BEARDED BULBOPHYLLUM
Bulbophyllum barbigerum
Shown here are the pseudobulbs, single leaves, inflorescences, and flowers. The flowers have an unpleasant odor.

ONCIDIUM TIGRINUM
Oncidium flowers are borne
in a wiry, spikelike partial
inflorescence.

COELOGYNE
Coelogyne parishii
This species is found in East
Asia and flowers in the
spring, producing sweet-
smelling blooms.

PAPHIOPEDILUM
Paphiopedilum concolor
An evergreen, terrestrial
orchid shown here with its
single flower, the labellum
pointing downward as the
ovary has been bent.

ORCHIDS

Column with
stigma and two
anthers

Almost
symmetrical
flower

APOSTASIA NUDA
Restricted to Southeast Asia and
northeast Australia, this species can be
recognized by its two or three anthers
and fingerlike sterile stamen.

BIRD'S NEST
ORCHID
Neottia nidus-avis
Widespread in Europe,
and parts of North Africa,
the Bird's Nest Orchid
lacks chorophyll and
depends on fungi
for nutrition.

Net-veined
leaf

ANOECTOCHILUS
ROXBURGHII
The orchid is shown here
displaying a flowering spike
bearing flowers.

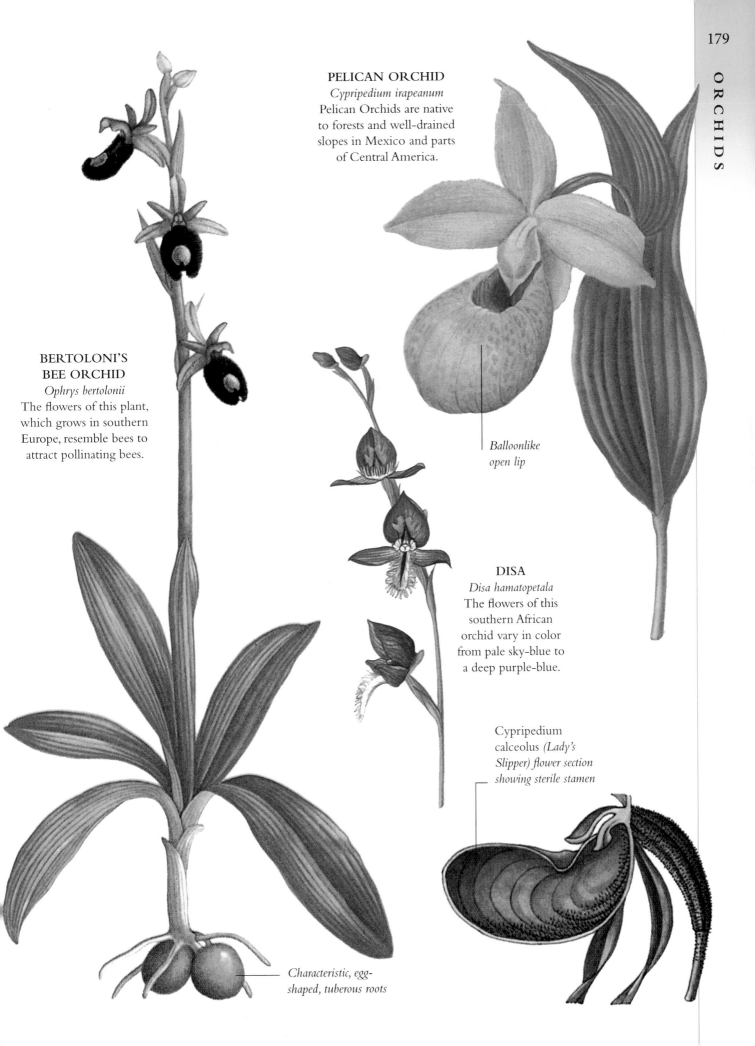

PELICAN ORCHID
Cypripedium irapeanum
Pelican Orchids are native
to forests and well-drained
slopes in Mexico and parts
of Central America.

*Balloonlike
open lip*

BERTOLONI'S
BEE ORCHID
Ophrys bertolonii
The flowers of this plant,
which grows in southern
Europe, resemble bees to
attract pollinating bees.

DISA
Disa hamatopetala
The flowers of this
southern African
orchid vary in color
from pale sky-blue to
a deep purple-blue.

*Cypripedium
calceolus (Lady's
Slipper) flower section
showing sterile stamen*

*Characteristic, egg-
shaped, tuberous roots*

GRASSES

In terms of their value to the world's economy, grasses (Poaceae) are the most important family of flowering plants. They grow on every continent, including one species in Antarctica. Grasses range from cereal crops such as wheat and barley to sugarcane, bamboo, and rice, with the last feeding more of the world's population than any other grass. Other grasses provide fodder for countless millions of domestic animals.

COMMON OAT
Avena sativa
Common Oat is a domesticated form of Wild Oat (*Avena sterilis*), which became widespread in Europe after the Bronze Age.

MEADOW BROOME
Bromus commutatus
This view shows a floret and a flower with three stamens.

PERENNIAL RYEGRASS
Lolium perenne
Ryegrass is a major component in many domestic lawns and has also been used for hundreds of years to sow pastures for livestock grazing.

OLYRA
Olyra ciliatifolia
The tip of this shoot shows broad leaves and a paniculate (much-branched) inflorescence.

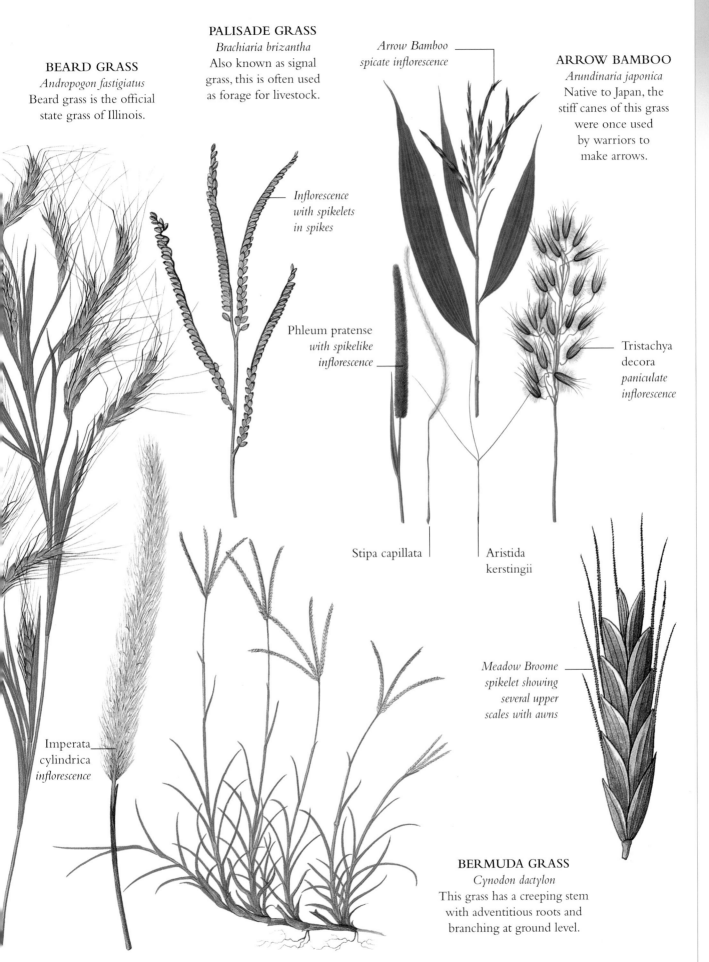

BEARD GRASS
Andropogon fastigiatus
Beard grass is the official
state grass of Illinois.

PALISADE GRASS
Brachiaria brizantha
Also known as signal
grass, this is often used
as forage for livestock.

*Inflorescence
with spikelets
in spikes*

*Arrow Bamboo
spicate inflorescence*

ARROW BAMBOO
Arundinaria japonica
Native to Japan, the
stiff canes of this grass
were once used
by warriors to
make arrows.

Phleum pratense
*with spikelike
inflorescence*

Tristachya
decora *paniculate
inflorescence*

Stipa capillata

Aristida
kerstingii

Imperata
cylindrica
inflorescence

*Meadow Broome
spikelet showing
several upper
scales with awns*

BERMUDA GRASS
Cynodon dactylon
This grass has a creeping stem
with adventitious roots and
branching at ground level.

WATER HYACINTHS AND PONDWEEDS

Water hyacinths form a small family
(Pontederiaceae) of freshwater aquatics
or marsh plants, which are widespread in
tropical and subtropical regions. Pondweeds
(Potamogetonaceae) grow in most regions of the
world. They spread rapidly and cause problems
when they clog up canals and other waterways.

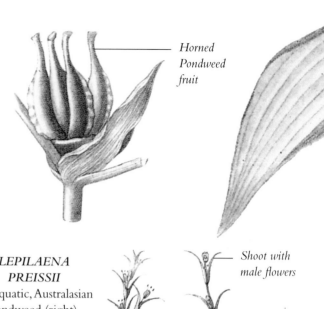

Horned
Pondweed
fruit

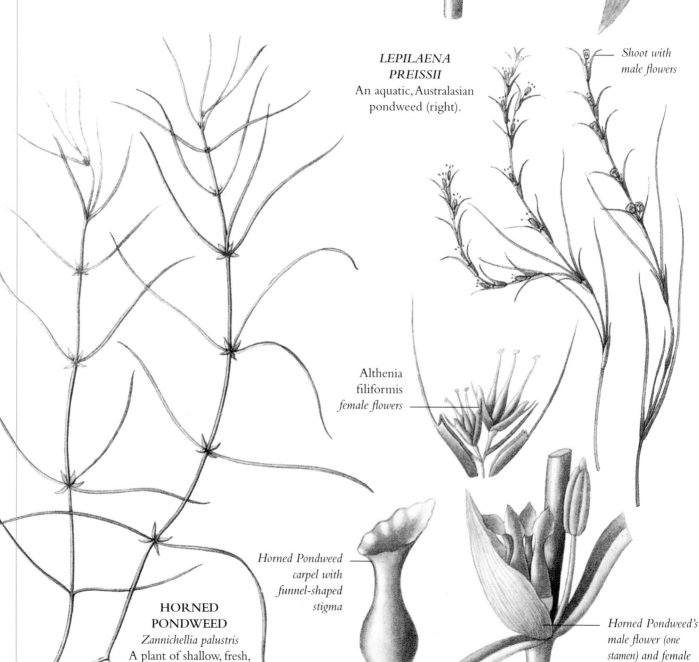

**LEPILAENA
PREISSII**
An aquatic, Australasian
pondweed (right).

Shoot with
male flowers

Althenia
filiformis
female flowers

Horned Pondweed
*carpel with
funnel-shaped
stigma*

**HORNED
PONDWEED**
Zannichellia palustris
A plant of shallow, fresh,
and brackish waters,
it has leaves up to
3 inches (8 cm) long.

Horned Pondweed's
*male flower (one
stamen) and female
flower (four carpels)*

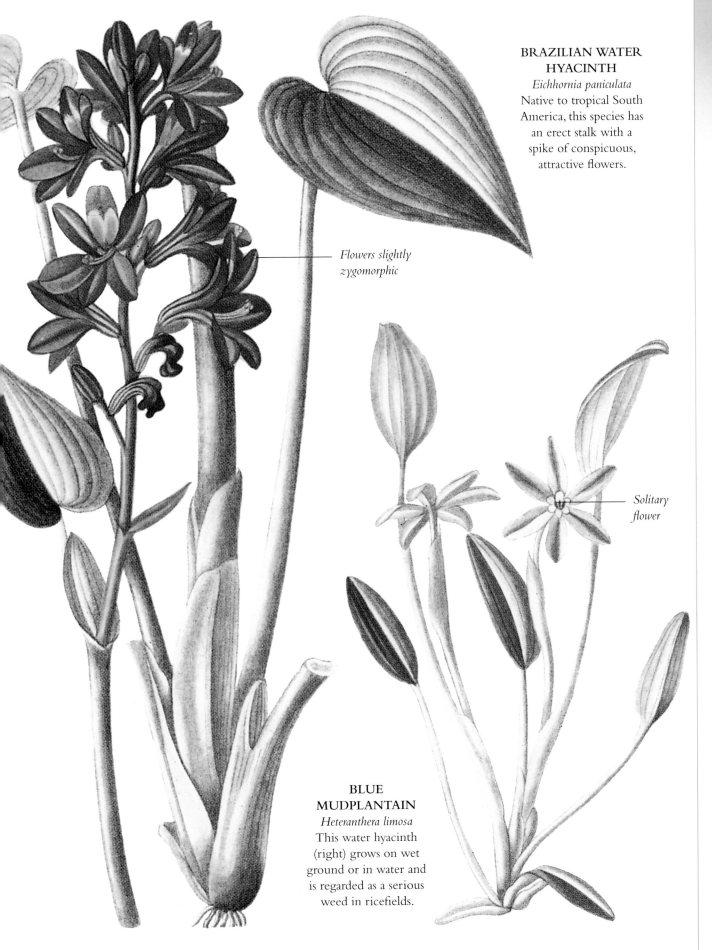

BRAZILIAN WATER HYACINTH
Eichhornia paniculata
Native to tropical South America, this species has an erect stalk with a spike of conspicuous, attractive flowers.

Flowers slightly zygomorphic

Solitary flower

BLUE MUDPLANTAIN
Heteranthera limosa
This water hyacinth (right) grows on wet ground or in water and is regarded as a serious weed in ricefields.

BIRDS-OF-PARADISE FLOWERS AND TECOPHILAS

The birds-of-paradise flowers (Strelitziaceae) are large herbs with big leaves and inflorescences, distinctive flowers, and conspicuous bracts. These plants grow along river banks or in swampy areas. Techophilas (Tecophilaeaceae) grow in sub-Saharan Africa and in Chile. While they prefer moist soil, they are known to be drought resistant.

Tough bract

BIRD-OF-PARADISE
Strelitzia reginae
Shown (right) is an inflorescence in a boat-shaped bract in which the flowers unfold in succession.

Smaller anterior stamens separate from single larger one

LADY'S HAND
Cyanella lutea
This perennial, terrestrial tecophila is native to southern Africa. Other tecophilas grow in the New World.

Corm

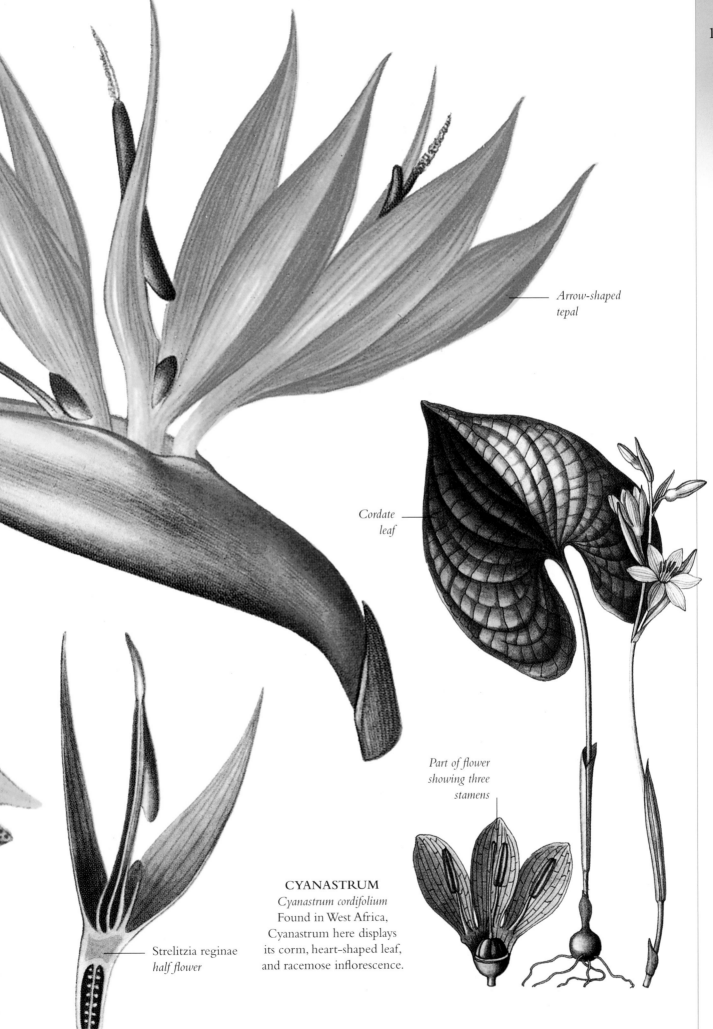

Arrow-shaped tepal

Cordate leaf

Part of flower showing three stamens

Strelitzia reginae *half flower*

CYANASTRUM

Cyanastrum cordifolium
Found in West Africa,
Cyanastrum here displays
its corm, heart-shaped leaf,
and racemose inflorescence.

RAPATEAS
AND RESTIOS

The tropical herbs of the Rapateaceae family are almost exclusively neotropical, the highest diversity occurring in the Amazon Basin. Rapateas grow mainly in bogs or swamps, as do the restios (Restionaceae). These evergreen, rushlike plants are found in southern Africa, Chile, and Australasia.

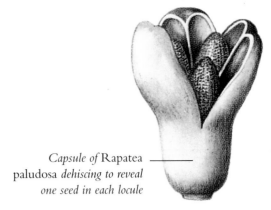

Capsule of Rapatea paludosa *dehiscing to reveal one seed in each locule*

Schoenocephalium arthrophyllum *showing linear, sheathing leaves and inflorescences*

Bract

RAPATEA PALUDOSA
This South African rapatea has an inflorescence with two subtending bracts.

Rapatea pandanoides *displays leaves with sheathing bases and petiole with short spines*

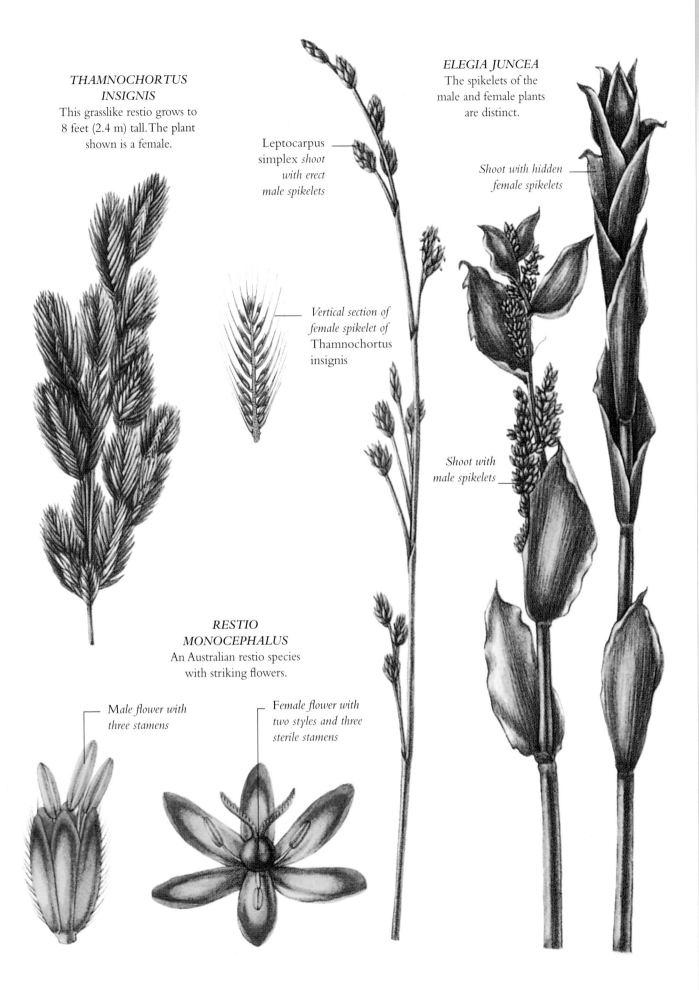

THAMNOCHORTUS INSIGNIS

This grasslike restio grows to 8 feet (2.4 m) tall. The plant shown is a female.

Leptocarpus simplex *shoot with erect male spikelets*

Vertical section of female spikelet of Thamnochortus insignis

ELEGIA JUNCEA

The spikelets of the male and female plants are distinct.

Shoot with hidden female spikelets

Shoot with male spikelets

RESTIO MONOCEPHALUS

An Australian restio species with striking flowers.

Male flower with three stamens

Female flower with two styles and three sterile stamens

GINGERS AND SCREWPINES

Gingers (Zingiberaceae) are aromatic, rhizomatous herbs, often with showy flowers. Turmeric, cardamom, galangal, and ginger itself are all products of this family. Screwpines (Pandanaceae) are tropical plants with long, spiny leaves and unisexual flowers.

GINGER SPECIES
Family Zingiberaceae
Most species in the ginger family grow in humid tropical lowlands.

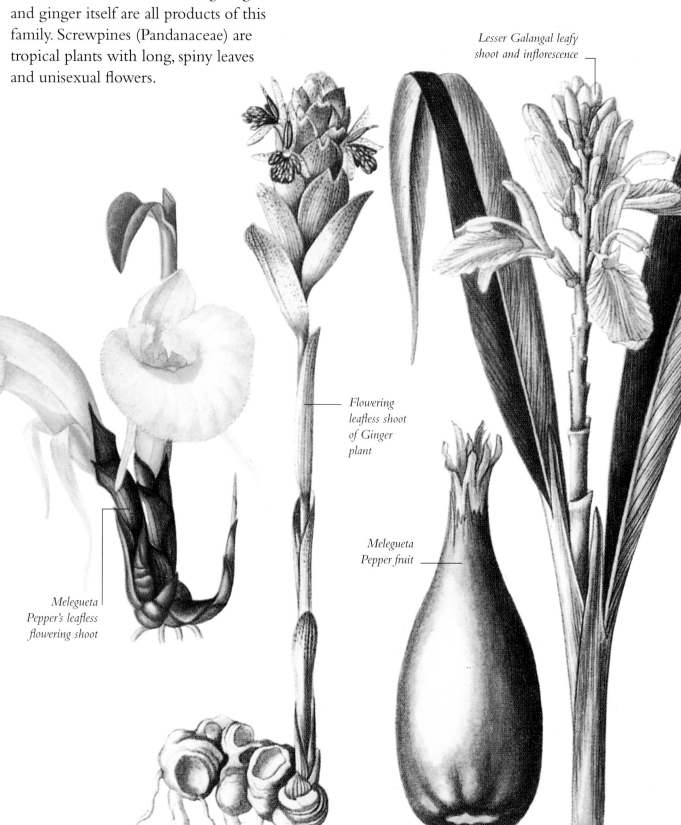

Lesser Galangal leafy shoot and inflorescence

Flowering leafless shoot of Ginger plant

Melegueta Pepper fruit

Melegueta Pepper's leafless flowering shoot

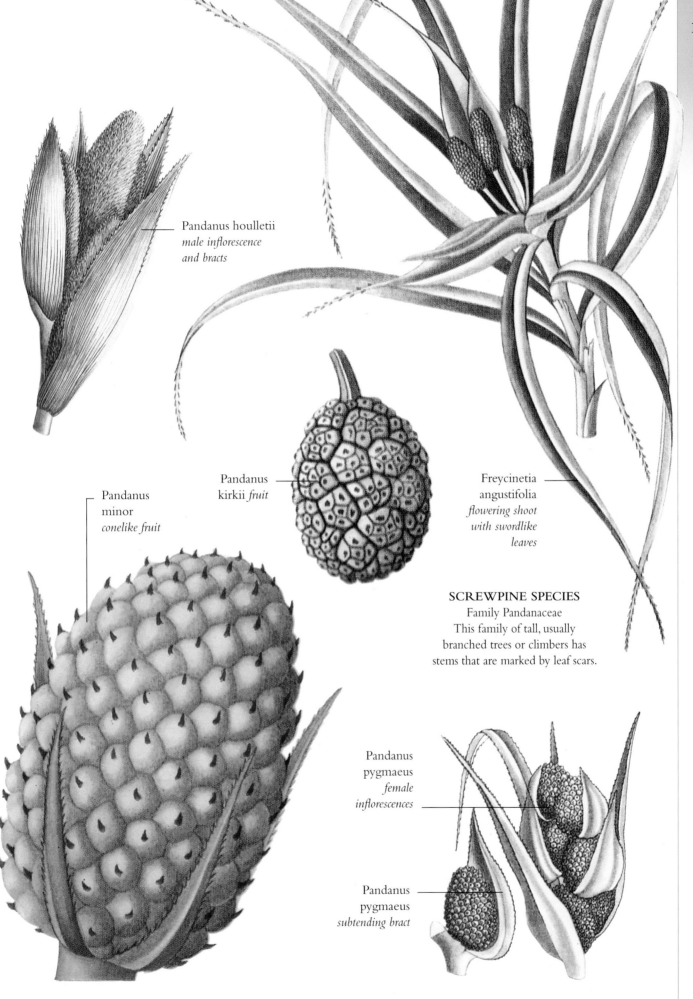

Pandanus houlletii
*male inflorescence
and bracts*

Pandanus
kirkii *fruit*

Freycinetia
angustifolia
*flowering shoot
with swordlike
leaves*

Pandanus
minor
conelike fruit

SCREWPINE SPECIES
Family Pandanaceae
This family of tall, usually
branched trees or climbers has
stems that are marked by leaf scars.

Pandanus
pygmaeus
*female
inflorescences*

Pandanus
pygmaeus
subtending bract

INDEX

Page numbers in **bold** refer to main entries.